Daily *warm-ups*

LOGIC

Louis Grant Brandes

WALCH PUBLISHING

Purchasers of this book are granted the right to reproduce all pages. This permission is limited to a single teacher, for classroom use only.

Any questions regarding this policy or requests to purchase further reproduction rights should be addressed to:

Permissions Editor
J. Weston Walch, Publisher
321 Valley Street • P.O. Box 658
Portland, Maine 04104-0658

Certified Chain of Custody
Promoting Sustainable
Forest Management
www.sfiprogram.org

SUSTAINABLE
FORESTRY
INITIATIVE

SGS-SFI/COC-US09/5501

1   2   3   4   5   6   7   8   9   10

ISBN 0-8251-5123-6

Copyright © 2004
Walch Publishing
P.O. Box 658 • Portland, Maine 04104-0658
walch.com
Printed in the United States of America

The *Daily Warm-Ups* series is a wonderful way to turn extra classroom minutes into valuable learning time. The 180 quick activities—one for each day of the school year—review, practice, and teach the principles of logic. These daily activities may be used at the very beginning of class to get students into learning mode, near the end of class to make good educational use of that transitional time, in the middle of class to shift gears between lessons—or whenever else you have minutes that now go unused. In addition to providing students with interesting logic problems, they are a natural path to other classroom activities involving critical thinking.

Daily Warm-Ups are easy-to-use reproducibles—simply photocopy the day's activity and distribute it. Or make a transparency of the activity and project it on the board. You may want to use the activities for extra-credit points or as a check on the logical and critical-thinking skills that are built and acquired over time.

However you choose to use them, *Daily Warm-Ups* are a convenient and useful supplement to your regular lesson plans. Make every minute of your class time count!

Birthday

Katya, a senior in high school, claims that her mother has only celebrated ten birthdays. If this is true, what is the date of her mother's birthday?

© 2004 Walch Publishing

Impossible Grip

Consider the following challenge: You must take something in your right hand that you can't possibly take in your left hand. What is this thing, and how is the challenge done?

2

© 2004 Walch Publishing

What Day Is Today?

When the day before yesterday was as far away from Thursday as the day after tomorrow will be from today, what day is today?

© 2004 Walch Publishing

Opposites

What is the opposite of "not in"?

4

© 2004 Walch Publishing

Changing Seven

How can you make seven even without adding or subtracting a number?

5

© 2004 Walch Publishing

Three Doubles

Chris, a bookkeeper who doesn't do much spelling, would like to know a word in which there are three double letters in succession. What is the word?

© 2004 Walch Publishing

Highest Mountain

What was the highest mountain before Mt. Everest was discovered?

Daily Warm-Ups: Logic

7

© 2004 Walch Publishing

The Perfume Bottle

A bottle of perfume costs $10. The perfume is worth $9 more than the bottle. What is the value of the bottle?

8

© 2004 Walch Publishing

Satia's Rest

Satia didn't get a wink of sleep for five days, yet she still didn't lack for rest. How is this possible?

9

© 2004 Walch Publishing

Jason's Walk

After walking 4 kilometers in a straight path, Jason found he'd traveled 2 kilometers in the opposite direction. Where was Jason when he stopped?

10

© 2004 Walch Publishing

Daily Warm-Ups: Logic

Upside-Down Digit

Which single-digit number increases in value when turned upside down?

© 2004 Walch Publishing

How Many Months?

How many months of the year have thirty days?

12

© 2004 Walch Publishing

Taking Pills

If you have three pills and take one every half hour, how long will they last?

13

© 2004 Walch Publishing

Even Apples

Jack Crowley had seven large apples that he divided equally among his three children. If no child received two or more chunks of apple, how did Jack accomplish this?

14

© 2004 Walch Publishing

Value of Money

Alexa has four current U.S. coins whose total value is more than 50¢ but less than $1. She does not have one or more coins that are exactly equal to 50¢. What coins does Alexa have?

15

© 2004 Walch Publishing

Pounds of Gold

Which is worth more: two pounds of $10 gold pieces or one pound of $20 gold pieces?

16

© 2004 Walch Publishing

Ancient Egyptian

An Egyptian was born on the first day of 30 B.C.E. and died on the first day of 30 C.E. For how many years did this Egyptian live?

Daily Warm-Ups: Logic

17

© 2004 Walch Publishing

Thick and Thin

How can you measure the thickness of a sheet of paper in your textbook with an ordinary ruler?

18

© 2004 Walch Publishing

Dry Spell

What is always sure to happen after a long dry spell?

© 2004 Walch Publishing

High Jump

What animal can jump as high as a house?

Under an Umbrella

Two women and a man were walking under an umbrella, yet none of them got wet. Why not?

21

© 2004 Walch Publishing

Running Water

When will water stop running downhill?

22

© 2004 Walch Publishing

Duck!

What does a baby duckling become when it first goes into the water?

23

© 2004 Walch Publishing

Goats

What do goats have that no other animals have?

24

© 2004 Walch Publishing

A Bucket

What can you put in a bucket to make it weigh less?

25

© 2004 Walch Publishing

Run, Don't Walk

Although this can run, it is unable to walk. What is it?

26

© 2004 Walch Publishing

Foot This Bill

What is bought by the yard and worn by the foot?

27

© 2004 Walch Publishing

Talking Back

Many have heard it, but nobody has ever seen it, and it will not speak back until spoken to. What is it?

28

© 2004 Walch Publishing

Fragile

This is neither big nor small. It is not a liquid, a solid, or a gas. Yet, it can be broken without being dropped. What is it?

Daily Warm-Ups: Logic

29

© 2004 Walch Publishing

Seeing Things

This has size and form and can be seen. Yet it cannot be felt, and it does not occupy space. What is it?

30

© 2004 Walch Publishing

Differences

What is the difference between a new dime and an old quarter?

31

© 2004 Walch Publishing

Which Month?

In which month do people talk the least?

32

© 2004 Walch Publishing

It's All Relative

Tomas told his friends, "My father and my grandfather are both celebrating their birthdays today. My father is 57. My grandfather is 50." How could this be true?

© 2004 Walch Publishing

Lost and Found

When you find something that you have lost, why is it that you always find it in the last place that you look?

34

© 2004 Walch Publishing

Form a Square: 1

The arrangement of lines below forms four squares. Move three lines (by striking out and redrawing) so that the arrangement forms three squares of equal size.

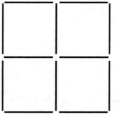

© 2004 Walch Publishing

Form a Square: 2

The arrangement of lines below forms four squares. Move four lines (by striking out and redrawing) so that the arrangement forms three squares of equal size.

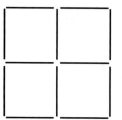

36

© 2004 Walch Publishing

Triangles and Squares

The arrangement of lines below forms four squares. Move three lines (by striking out and redrawing) so that the arrangement forms six triangles of equal size.

Daily Warm-Ups: Logic

© 2004 Walch Publishing

Forming Triangles

The arrangement of lines below forms two squares. Move two lines (by striking out and redrawing) so that the arrangement forms three triangles of equal size.

38

© 2004 Walch Publishing

Daily Warm-Ups: Logic

Three into Four

The arrangement of lines below forms three triangles. Move two lines (by striking out and redrawing) so that the arrangement forms four triangles of equal size.

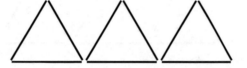

39

© 2004 Walch Publishing

Four Out of Three

The arrangement of lines below forms three triangles. Move three lines (by striking out and redrawing) so that the arrangement forms four triangles of equal size.

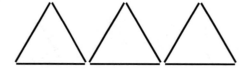

40

© 2004 Walch Publishing

Three into One

The arrangement of lines below forms three triangles. Move four lines (by striking out and redrawing) so that the arrangement forms one large triangle.

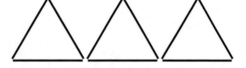

Daily Warm-Ups: Logic

© 2004 Walch Publishing

41

Dividing a Figure

The arrangement of lines below forms a six-sided polygon. Add eight lines to divide it into four equal parts, all of which are the same shape.

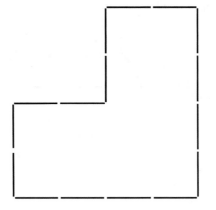

© 2004 Walch Publishing

Daily Warm-Ups: Logic

Changing Face

The lines below form the outline of a barn that faces left. Move two lines (by striking out and redrawing) so that the barn seems to face right.

© 2004 Walch Publishing

A Peculiar Thing

The more you take away, the larger it gets. As you add to it, it gets smaller and smaller. What peculiar thing is this?

44

© 2004 Walch Publishing

One, Two, Zero

What is it that occurs once in a minute, twice in a moment, and not once in a thousand years?

45

© 2004 Walch Publishing

How Many Children?

Philip and Danae were talking about their families. Danae said, "Each boy in my family has as many brothers as he has sisters. But each girl in my family has twice as many brothers as sisters."

How many boys and girls are in Danae's family?

46

© 2004 Walch Publishing

That Which Is Most Unusual

It is not a solid, a liquid, a gas, a mineral, an animal, or a vegetable. It is constantly moving wherever it exists. It can reproduce itself, yet it is not alive and never was. It is very important for people's existence, and it is extremely common. What is it?

47

© 2004 Walch Publishing

Vacation Plans

Before going on a vacation, Carolina was asked how long she planned to be away. She answered, "When it is the day after tomorrow, I will be able to say that I shall start a week from yesterday. I'm not planning to come back until four weeks from the day before yesterday." How long does Carolina plan to be away?

48

© 2004 Walch Publishing

Tom and Jerry

If Tom's father is Jerry's son, how is Jerry related to Tom?

49

© 2004 Walch Publishing

The Widow's Sister

There is no law against it, but it is not possible for a man to marry his widow's sister. Can you explain why not?

50

© 2004 Walch Publishing

Big and Little

A big polar bear and a little polar bear are sitting on a block of ice. If the little bear is the son of the big bear, but the big bear is not the father of the little bear, what is the relationship between the two?

51

© 2004 Walch Publishing

Aunt and Nephew

Raquel and Luis are aunt and nephew, respectively. "How can you be my aunt?" Luis inquires. "Although we're blood relatives, we're both the same age!" How is this possible?

52

© 2004 Walch Publishing

A Father's Son

A man points to his son and says, "Brothers and sisters have I none, but this man's father is my father's son."

Can you explain this statement?

© 2004 Walch Publishing

The Two Sisters

Two sisters are walking down the street. One of them says, "I want to stop by the school for a few minutes to see my nephew." The other replies, "Since I have no nephew, I will walk on ahead." How could this be true?

54

© 2004 Walch Publishing

Brothers and Sisters

A man and his wife have three children between them. The husband has a daughter by a former marriage; the wife also has a daughter by a former marriage. They have a son by their current marriage. What is the relationship of the children?

Daily Warm-Ups: Logic

© 2004 Walch Publishing

An Old Photograph

A young man and his sister were looking at an old photo album. The young man pointed to a photograph of a woman and explained, "This woman's father was my father's brother-in-law." What relation was the young man's sister to the subject in the photograph?

56

© 2004 Walch Publishing

The Portrait of a Woman

As they were walking through their old family home, a man looked up and pointed to a portrait of a woman. He said to his son, "That woman's mother was my father's mother-in-law." What is the relationship of the man to the subject of the portrait?

57

© 2004 Walch Publishing

A Family Reunion

A family gathering included one grandfather, one grandmother, two fathers, two mothers, four children, three grandchildren, one brother, two sisters, two sons, two daughters, one father-in-law, one mother-in-law, and one daughter-in-law. This made a total of seven people. Can you explain how this is possible?

58

© 2004 Walch Publishing

A Magic Trick

A performer borrowed a half-dollar coin and a dollar bill from two members of her audience. She put the coin in her right hand and the dollar bill in her left hand. Then she closed her hands tightly around the money and held them about a foot apart. Next, she announced that she would make the money change places without again opening her hands. She did! How did the performer accomplish this?

59

© 2004 Walch Publishing

Dish Trick

The host of a party placed three empty dishes, all of equal size, on top of a table. He then put ten pieces of candy near the dishes. He challenged his guests to place the candy in the three dishes so that each dish contained an odd number of pieces. Can you explain how the guests met the challenge?

60

© 2004 Walch Publishing

Take Away One and Get One More

One day a teacher asked her class, "Did you know that you can take one from four and leave five . . . and take one from five and leave six?" She took a blank sheet of paper and held it up before the class. "You will note," she said, "that this sheet of paper has four corners. Does anyone know how I can take one corner away and have five corners left?"

Getting no response, she showed how this could be done. Can you explain what she did?

61

© 2004 Walch Publishing

Accomplishing the Impossible

A teacher entered his classroom wearing a very flashy hat. When he was sure that he had the attention of the entire class, he removed the hat. Then, holding it up for all to see, he announced, "You really don't know how unusual this hat is!"

He put the hat on his desk, picked up a sheet of paper, and cut a small hole in the center of the paper. "I can actually fold the hat," he continued, "and push it through the hole in this sheet of paper." Thereupon he put the sheet of paper on the desk, picked up the hat, and carefully folded it one time before returning it to the desk.

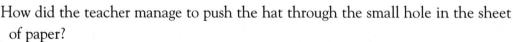

How did the teacher manage to push the hat through the small hole in the sheet of paper?

62

© 2004 Walch Publishing

One Word From Two Words

Coming into his classroom a few minutes late, a teacher walked to the board and wrote, in large letters, *NEW DOOR*. Then he turned to the class and said, "I would like to see if anyone in this class can use the seven letters I have written on the board to write one word." With this, he turned his attention to the business of taking attendance and otherwise getting ready for the class lesson.

When five minutes had passed, no student had found the answer. The teacher then wrote the solution on the board. What was his solution?

Daily Warm-Ups: Logic

© 2004 Walch Publishing

Full and Empty Glasses

Place six water glasses in a row. The first three glasses should be filled with water; the second three glasses should be empty. You must rearrange the glasses in the row so that they are alternately one filled, one empty, one filled, and so on. This must be done by touching only one glass. Can you explain how to do this?

64

© 2004 Walch Publishing

How Many Spots?

A magician placed four dice in a clear glass. Then she put her hand over the open end and held the glass between her palms. After shaking the glass so that the dice jumped about, she asked a member of the audience to look up through the lower part of the glass and count the spots on the bottoms of the dice. After this had been done, she told the audience that she already knew the total, although she couldn't see the bottom sides of the dice. Can you explain how the magician was able to do this?

Daily Warm-Ups: Logic

65

© 2004 Walch Publishing

A Trick of Digit Addition

111   999   777

The three sets of digits above (three 1s, three 9s, and three 7s) make a total of nine digits. The object is to cross out six of the digits and leave three digits whose sum is eighteen. Can you manage this?

Daily Warm-Ups: Logic

66

© 2004 Walch Publishing

Old Coin

A member of an ancient-history class brought in a coin marked 439 B.C.E. Members of the class were very excited about handling such an unusual relic, until one student pointed out that it was a fake. After she explained herself, the entire class agreed that it was a fake coin. What convinced the class that the coin was a fake?

Daily Warm-Ups: Logic

67

© 2004 Walch Publishing

The Fake Explorer

A man billed as a famous explorer was telling his audience how he once shot a polar bear as it was chasing penguins across an ice floe. Suddenly an audience member stood up and shouted, "You're a fake!" What led this audience member to conclude that the speaker was a fake?

68

© 2004 Walch Publishing

The Chemists

Cho and Anna were partners in a small chemical plant. One day Cho went over to Anna, carefully carrying a glass vial of a bubbling solution.

"I've finally done it!" Cho announced. "I have in this vial a substance that will quickly dissolve any solid it touches. We'll be rich!"

"You're dreaming again," Anna replied. "How could you make such a foolish claim?"

What made Anna so sure that Cho was wrong about the solution?

69

© 2004 Walch Publishing

An Unusual Accomplishment

Desirée took a rubber ball and threw it with all her might. The ball stopped and came right back to her without hitting the ground, a wall, or any other obstruction, and without having anything attached to it. Can you explain Desirée's feat?

70

© 2004 Walch Publishing

Pocket Money

Talia and Erin were going to the dollar store. Erin suggested that they pool their money and share it equally. Talia said, "If you can guess how much money I have, I'll pool it with yours. I already know how much money you have. If you gave me one dollar, I'd have twice as much money as you. If I gave you one dollar, we'd both have the same amount." How much money does each girl have?

Daily Warm-Ups: Logic

© 2004 Walch Publishing

A Light Mystery

Your bedroom is six meters square, with two windows on one side. The bed is against a wall away from the windows and across from the door. The light switch for the only light in the room is near the door and three meters from the bed. How is it possible to switch off the light and get into bed before the room is dark?

72

© 2004 Walch Publishing

Pasturing the Horses

A rancher has a herd of eighteen horses and three fields to use as pastures. An eccentricity of the rancher is that he does not want an even number of horses placed in any one field. How can the rancher divide his horses under these conditions?

Daily Warm-Ups: Logic

73

© 2004 Walch Publishing

A Ship's Ladder

A ship is anchored offshore. It has a wire ladder, with rungs that are three decimeters apart, hanging over the side. The bottom rung is resting on the surface of the harbor. An incoming tide is rising at the rate of 20 centimeters an hour. At the rate of the steadily incoming tide, how long will it take the first four rungs of the ladder to be covered with water?

74

© 2004 Walch Publishing

Predicting the Weather

It rained all day yesterday, and it is raining now at midnight. Considering that it rains less than one fourth of the time during this season of the year, do you feel that there is a good chance that it will be a sunny day in seventy-two hours? Answer this question with a *yes* or *no*, and justify your answer.

Daily Warm-Ups: Logic

75

© 2004 Walch Publishing

Seeing Is Believing?

If someone told you that the top line on the left of the figure below is the one extended on the right, would you believe it? How could you find out whether this is true?

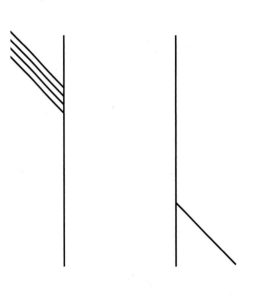

76

© 2004 Walch Publishing

Guarding a Watermelon Field

Karla and Hamdi were hired to guard a watermelon field. Looking in opposite directions, they had a clear view of the field. Suddenly, without moving his head, Hamdi asked, "Karla, why are you making such a weird face?"

How did Hamdi know, without turning his head, that Karla was making an odd face?

Daily Warm-Ups: Logic

© 2004 Walch Publishing

The Visiting Farmer

A farmer was visiting his relatives in the city. They asked him how many animals he had on his farm. Wanting to impress them, he replied, "There are all horses but three, all cows but three, all pigs but three, all goats but three." According to the farmer's statement, how many animals did he have?

78

© 2004 Walch Publishing

Who Gets the Most Rain?

A resident of a large city was visiting a rural area. He stopped to talk with one of the locals and, to make conversation, asked, "Do you get much rain out here?"

"We get some, but not very much," the man replied, shaking his head sadly. After some hesitation, he added, "My neighbor across the road always gets a lot more rain than I get."

The city man was very puzzled. "I don't understand," he replied. "How could your neighbor, who is just across the road from you, get more rain than you?"

As odd as this may seem, it was true. Can you explain how it was possible?

Daily Warm-Ups: Logic

79

© 2004 Walch Publishing

Gasohol

A man has two tanks of equal size. The first is half full of gasoline, and the second is half full of alcohol. The man takes a pint of gasoline from the first tank and mixes it thoroughly with the alcohol in the second tank. He then takes a pint of this mixture from the second tank and mixes it with the gasoline in the first tank. After this mixing has been completed, is there more or less alcohol in the first tank than there is gasoline in the second tank?

A Word That Is Pronounced Wrong

A judge in a U.S. court of law must be very careful in choosing words. It is also important to pronounce every word correctly. All judges are aware of this. There is one word, however, that every judge pronounces wrong, including each of the judges of the Supreme Court. The word is a common one that every alert student should recognize. What is this one word?

81

© 2004 Walch Publishing

Dividing the Oranges

A woman said, "As I was walking home from a store where I had been shopping, I was met by two fathers who were with two sons. We stopped and talked for a while. As I was about to leave them, I reached into my shopping bag and gave them three large oranges. When they had divided the oranges among themselves, each had a whole orange." Can you explain how this was possible?

82

© 2004 Walch Publishing

The Young Man With a Dirty Face

Two young men spent the morning exploring an old mine shaft. When they came out of the mine into the bright daylight, the face of one young man was covered with dirt; the face of the other was clean. Neither man said a word. The young man with the clean face immediately walked to a nearby stream and washed his face. The man with the dirty face stayed by the mine. Can you explain why the young man with the clean face went to the stream to wash?

Daily Warm-Ups: Logic

83

© 2004 Walch Publishing

The Doctor's Son

Mr. Britos and his son Jaime were involved in a plane crash. The father died at the scene of the crash. The son, who was critically injured, was rushed by ambulance to a nearby hospital. The doctor on duty in the emergency room took one look at the boy and said, "I can't work on this patient. He is my son." How could Jaime be the doctor's son?

84

© 2004 Walch Publishing

True or False?

Mark each statement below as either true or false.

___ 1. Exactly one statement in this list is false.

___ 2. Exactly two statements in this list are false.

___ 3. Exactly three statements in this list are false.

___ 4. Exactly four statements in this list are false.

___ 5. Exactly five statements in this list are false.

85

© 2004 Walch Publishing

The Robbery

Before he left his apartment, Jamal carefully secured all the windows and examined the lock of the only door. He then left to visit his girlfriend. When he returned later that night, he found his room ransacked; his computer, stereo, and television set were missing. He was sure that the door had been locked when he arrived home. The windows had not been unlocked or broken. The burglar, who was later captured by the police, insisted that he had used no burglary tools or keys. How could the burglar have gotten into Jamal's apartment?

86

© 2004 Walch Publishing

The Antique Clocks

A woman whose hobby was collecting timepieces bought two antique clocks. After working on them for many days, she still could not get them to keep time properly. One of the clocks did not work at all; the other lost four minutes every day. The woman wanted to know which of the two clocks was more often correct. How could someone explain this for her?

87

© 2004 Walch Publishing

The Girls Who Look Alike

On the first day of school, two girls appeared in class who looked exactly alike and dressed exactly alike. The teacher noted on the enrollment cards that they had the same dates of birth, lived at the same address, and had the same last names.

As a matter of greeting, the teacher said to the first girl, "You must be sisters."

The first girl replied, "Yes, we are sisters."

The teacher then said to the second girl, "I take it that you two are twins."

The second girl replied, "No, we are not twins."

Assuming that each of the girls answered truthfully, how is this possible?

88

© 2004 Walch Publishing

Daily Warm-Ups: Logic

A Broken Limb

Paul, who was a sophomore in college, was writing his weekly letter home. He started his letter by stating, "I walked home from the doctor's office today, after I was taken there from football practice. I had bad luck and broke a limb during practice."

When his parents read the letter a few days later, they reasoned that a limb could mean either a leg or an arm. They were able to tell whether it was a right arm, left arm, left leg, or right leg. How did Paul's parents know which limb he had broken?

Daily Warm-Ups: Logic

© 2004 Walch Publishing

The Monkey and the Pulley

A rope is passed over a frictionless pulley, which is suspended from a rafter. On the rafter, directly above the pulley, there is a bunch of bananas. On one end of the rope there is a weight that exactly balances the weight of a monkey that is on the other end. The monkey is trying to climb up the rope in order to reach the bananas.

Now that you have all the facts, here is the question: As the monkey climbs the rope, will he rise above the weight or sink below it?

© 2004 Walch Publishing

The Hungry Bookworm

There are five volumes in a set of books placed in order on a library shelf. Each volume of the set is five centimeters thick. A bookworm starts on the first page of volume I and eats through to the last page of volume V. If the thickness of the covers is disregarded, through what distance does the bookworm eat?

Daily Warm-Ups: Logic

© 2004 Walch Publishing

Getting the Traveler Across the River

A mountain man is making his annual trip to town to buy supplies and visit with friends. He comes to a river, which he must cross. His possessions include a pet wolf, a goat, and a sack of carrots. The only available boat with which to cross the river is very small; it can carry no more than the traveler and one of his possessions at a time.

The man realizes that if left together, the goat will eat the carrots and the wolf will dine on the goat. How can he transport his belongings to the other side of the river and still keep them intact?

92

© 2004 Walch Publishing

The Police and the Prisoners

In a far-off land, three police officers and three prisoners became lost. All were unarmed. When they came to a river that they had to cross, all agreed to travel together peacefully. To cross the river, they found a small boat, which would hold only two people. The prisoners seemed friendly enough. However, the police didn't want to be outnumbered by them at any point, even if it meant losing the prisoners.

How did all six of these people get across the river in the boat without the prisoners outnumbering the police at any time?

93

© 2004 Walch Publishing

Planes to Detroit and Boston

Airplanes A and B leave at the same time. Airplane A is going from Boston to Detroit; Airplane B is heading from Detroit to Boston. Airplane A averages 150 kilometers per hour; Airplane B averages 200 kilometers per hour.

Assuming that it is 1,200 air kilometers from Boston to Detroit, which airplane will be closer to Detroit when the two planes pass? (Compute to the nearest kilometer.)

© 2004 Walch Publishing

Is Honolulu Nearer the Sun at Noon Than It Is at Sunset?

Johnny Kalulu, who lives in Honolulu, Hawaii, made what he thought was a startling discovery as he was meditating while walking home from school one day. He noted that Honolulu was more than 6,000 kilometers closer to the sun at noon than it was at sunset. Is it possible that Johnny's discovery was correct?

95

A Missed Direction

How on earth could a person take a hike by walking 5 kilometers due north, 5 kilometers due west, and 5 kilometers due south, only to return to her exact starting spot?

96

© 2004 Walch Publishing

What Day Is It?

You are sent in an airplane on a scientific mission. You leave Chicago on Monday at 8:00 A.M. and fly due north for six hours. At this time, you jump from the plane and land exactly on the North Pole. What day is it at the point where you land?

Daily Warm-Ups: Logic

97

© 2004 Walch Publishing

Northern Exposure

A husband and wife are planning to build a rectangular house with windows on all sides. After talking it over, they decide that they would like all the windows to have a northern exposure. Would it be possible to build such a house?

98

© 2004 Walch Publishing

A Fox and a Bear

A fox, happily hunting for his morning meal, spotted a huge bear some distance due east of him. Terrified of becoming a tasty morsel for the bear, the fox ran due north for an equal distance before realizing that the bear had not seen him. The fox then stopped and remained hidden. Although the fox didn't realize it, at this point the bear was due south of him.

Now that we can assume that the fox is still safely alive, can you tell the color of the bear?

99

© 2004 Walch Publishing

A Missing Dollar

Two band members were selling candy bars for their school to raise money for new uniforms. Each band member had thirty candy bars to sell. One band member sold the candy bars for 50¢ each; the other band member sold the candy bars at three for $1. At the end of the day, after selling all of their candy bars, their earnings were $15 and $10, respectively, or a total of $25.

Since one band member had sold the bars at the rate of two for $1, and the other band member had sold the bars at the rate of three for $1, they decided the next day to pool the same number of candy bars—a total of sixty—and sell them at the rate of five for $2. After selling all their candy bars on the second day, the band members checked their earnings and found that they had only $24. They searched everywhere for one more dollar, each thinking that the other must have it.

How were the band members going to explain the missing dollar at school?

© 2004 Walch Publishing

Five Liters of Water

A man with a 3-liter jar and a 4-liter jar went to a well to get exactly 5 liters of water. He had no containers other than the two jars. How could the man get the 5 liters of water?

101

© 2004 Walch Publishing

Dividing the Juice

Two friends have an 8-liter jug full of juice that they wish to share equally. They have two empty jars; one has a capacity of 5 liters, and the other has a capacity of 3 liters. They plan to divide the juice between them without spilling a drop. Can you explain how the friends plan to divide the juice?

102

© 2004 Walch Publishing

The Same Color Socks

A family of four went on a camping trip. They stayed at a remote site in a national park. One family member decided to get an early start one morning, so she arose quietly and started dressing. She didn't want to use a light for fear of waking the others. Everything went fine until it was time to put on her socks. She knew that she had four blue socks and four white socks in the bottom of her duffel bag. However, she didn't know the least number of socks that she could take out of the bag to be sure of having two of the same color before leaving the tent to put them on. How many socks did she have to take out of the bag to be sure of a matching pair?

103

© 2004 Walch Publishing

The Missing Dollars

Three journalists, arriving late one night at a motel, were charged $80 each for a room, or $240 in all. Later, the motel manager, thinking that she had overcharged, decided to refund $40 of the money to the guests. She sent the money by her son, who was alert enough to observe that $40 could not be divided equally among three people. Thus, the boy kept $16 for himself and returned $24 to the journalists. Each journalist happily received $8 back, making the rooms cost $72 each, or a total of $216 collectively.

Since together the journalists paid a sum of $216 for the rooms and the boy kept $16, for a total of $232, what happened to the other $8?

Daily Warm-Ups: Logic

104

© 2004 Walch Publishing

The Appointment

A man, who has a doctor's appointment for himself and his two small sons, finds that his car will not start. Since the doctor's office is fairly far away, they cannot walk and get there on time. A bicycle, which they own, cannot hold all of them, but it will carry either the man or the two boys.

The man and his two sons actually do make their doctor's appointment on time. Can you explain how they use the bicycle to do this?

Daily Warm-Ups: Logic

© 2004 Walch Publishing

The Liar's Dilemma

Liars never tell the truth. I am a liar. This means that if I am a liar, I am telling the truth, and therefore I am not a liar. If I am not a liar, then I am not telling the truth, and therefore I am a liar.

Are these statements logical?

106

© 2004 Walch Publishing

Turning the Glasses

Three water glasses are arranged on a table top as shown below. A move of the glasses consists of turning over two glasses simultaneously, one with each hand.

You are challenged to bring all of the glasses upright in exactly three such moves.

107

© 2004 Walch Publishing

Choosing the Correct Twin

Sally's boyfriend had an identical twin whom she did not like. Her boyfriend always told the truth, and his twin always lied. One evening, one of the twins came to visit her. Since the twins looked exactly alike, she couldn't tell whether he was her truth-telling boyfriend or the liar. Sally thought for a moment, then asked the visitor one question. From the reply, she knew which twin was visiting her. What was the question that Sally asked?

108

© 2004 Walch Publishing

The Mismarked Fruit Baskets

Three baskets in a fruit market are marked *Oranges*, *Grapefruit*, and *Oranges and Grapefruit*. Suppose that you cannot see the fruit in the baskets, but you are told that each basket is marked incorrectly. However, the baskets *collectively* contain the fruits described on the labels.

You can select only one piece of fruit from only one of the baskets. From the single piece of fruit that you select, how would you know enough to be able to relabel each basket correctly?

109

© 2004 Walch Publishing

A Test of Honesty

A man is known to do one of the following: (1) always tell the truth, (2) never tell the truth, or (3) make statements that are alternately true and false, or false and true.

In two questions, each answered by a *Yes* or a *No*, how might you determine whether this man tells the truth, is a liar, or alternates with true and false answers?

110

© 2004 Walch Publishing

A Matter of Life or Death

An unscrupulous old sultan, wishing to be rid of one of his advisers, put two pieces of paper in a hat. He told a watching magistrate that if the adviser drew out the piece of paper marked *LIFE*, he would be set free, but if he drew out the piece of paper marked *DEATH*, he must die. The sultan then wrote *DEATH* on both pieces of paper. However, when the adviser—who had been living by his wits for many years—showed the magistrate one piece of paper, the magistrate decided in his favor.

How did the adviser outwit the old sultan?

© 2004 Walch Publishing

Which Tribe?

An anthropologist was rowing up a stream in the wilds of a remote land where she knew the Waho and Tabo tribes lived. She knew that the Waho always told the truth, but that the Tabo always lied. As she rounded a bend in the river, she saw three men on the nearby riverbank. She directed a question to the first of the three men: "Are you a Waho, or a Tabo?"

The man answered, but the anthropologist could not understand what he had said. In the meantime, the second of the three men added, "He said that he is a Waho, and he tells the truth."

The third man then said, "The second man who spoke is a Tabo."

The anthropologist was able to tell to which tribe each man belonged. How did she know this?

112

© 2004 Walch Publishing

The Traveler Saves His Life

Many years ago, a traveler passing through a foreign kingdom was captured by the soldiers of a mean, old king. When he appeared before the king, the traveler was condemned to death. As a way of amusing himself and his followers, the king announced to the condemned man, "You have an opportunity to make one statement. If the statement is true, you will be beheaded on the spot. If the statement is false, you will be roasted alive. Otherwise, you will be set free."

When the traveler made his statement, the mean, old king muttered to himself for a few moments, then set the traveler free. What did the traveler say?

113

© 2004 Walch Publishing

The Accuser

Mr. Gomez was quite wealthy as a young man, but he was cheated out of all his money. He became a bitter old man, living on a tiny pension.

As Mr. Gomez lay on his deathbed, he asked three lawyers, who had worked with him during better times, to visit him. Their names were Chang, Johnson, and Gould. As the three lawyers walked through the doorway of his hospital room, Mr. Gomez sat upright in bed. Staring directly at the visitors, he said, "*He* did it, the dirty swindler." Then he fell back in the bed, and with a groan, he died.

Why was it obvious that it was Johnson who had been accused?

114

© 2004 Walch Publishing

Dividing a Cake

There is an old way of making sure that a cake is divided to the mutual satisfaction of two people. That is to let one of the two people who are to share the cake cut it; the other person gets first choice of the two pieces.

Using the same theory of letting the people who will be eating the cake divide it, how can a cake be divided to the mutual satisfaction of three people?

Daily Warm-Ups: Logic

© 2004 Walch Publishing

Three Friends

Leah, Nikki, and Clara, who are close friends, love sports. However, only two of them kayak, only two of them play lacrosse, and only two of them play tennis.

1. Leah doesn't play lacrosse.

2. Nikki plays tennis, but doesn't play one of Leah's games.

Name the games that each young woman plays.

116

© 2004 Walch Publishing

The Nicknames

Four friends named Hannah, Ben, Owen, and Anisa are in a chat room. Their screen names are Animefan, Anonymous, Sportsgirl, and Rockster. One day, while talking among themselves, they make the following statements:

1. Hannah says, "I'm older than Sportsgirl and younger than Rockster."

2. Ben says, "I live next door to Sportsgirl, and I don't like anime."

3. Rockster says, "I'm shorter than Owen and taller than Anonymous."

What is the screen name of each person?

Daily Warm-Ups: Logic

117

© 2004 Walch Publishing

High School Classes

Josh, Chelsea, Luisa, and Hamdi are students at the same high school. They are in the freshman, sophomore, junior, and senior classes, but not necessarily in the order of their names above. The following statements are true about these students:

1. Chelsea is in a class below Luisa and above Hamdi.

2. Luisa is in a class above Hamdi and below Josh.

In which class is each of the students?

118

© 2004 Walch Publishing

The Basketball Players

Li, Talia, and Ashley play on the girls' varsity basketball team of their school. The young women's positions are forward, guard, and center, but not necessarily in the order of their names above. The following additional facts are known:

1. Talia and the center have each scored more points to date than Ashley.

2. Talia is not the forward.

Who plays each position?

Daily Warm-Ups: Logic

119

© 2004 Walch Publishing

School Faculty

Ms. Chang, Mr. Pejcek, and Ms. Taylor are members of a high-school faculty. Their titles are counselor, principal, and teacher, but not necessarily in the order of their names above. The following additional facts are known about these people:

1. No person's name begins with the same first letter as that of his or her title.

2. Mr. Pejcek is not the counselor.

What is the title of each of the three faculty members?

© 2004 Walch Publishing

What's for Lunch?

During the school lunch hour, students Hosea, Juanita, and Ramon ate lunch together. One had a veggie burger, one had a toasted cheese sandwich, and one had a fajita. The following observations apply to what they were eating:

1. Ramon did not have the toasted cheese sandwich or the fajita.

2. Juanita did not have the toasted cheese sandwich.

What did each of the students have for lunch?

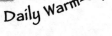

© 2004 Walch Publishing

Identifying the Students

Two students, a girl and a boy, are sitting on a bench outside the school.

"I'm a girl," said the one with blond hair.

"I'm a boy," said the one with black hair.

If at least one of the two students is lying, which person has blond hair and which one has black hair?

122

© 2004 Walch Publishing

Track Meet

At a track meet, six young women were competing in a race. As the winner broke the tape at the finish line, the following conditions existed:

1. Imani was 25 meters behind Alyssa.

2. Alyssa was 15 meters ahead of Kate.

3. Midori was running alongside Aileen.

4. Kate was 30 meters behind Sara, who was 5 meters ahead of Aileen.

List the order in which the girls were running when the winner crossed the finish line.

© 2004 Walch Publishing

Relative to a Conversation

At a family reunion, two couples were having separate conversations. Serena and Nick were talking to each other, and Hawa and Kai were talking to each other.

Serena said to Nick, "That boy, Kai, is my nephew."

Nick replied to Serena, "Yes, but he is not my nephew."

Hawa asked Kai, "Is Serena married?"

Kai replied to Hawa, "No, but she is Nick's sister."

On the basis of these conversations, what relation is Kai to Nick?

124

© 2004 Walch Publishing

Catching a Plane

Emily, Rachel, Ari, and Alicia have plans to catch a two o'clock plane.

Emily's watch is five minutes slow, but she thinks it's ten minutes fast.

Rachel's watch is five minutes fast, but she thinks it's ten minutes slow.

Ari's watch is ten minutes slow, but she thinks it's ten minutes fast.

Alicia's watch is ten minutes fast, but she thinks it's five minutes slow.

Each woman leaves home to catch the plane so that she will just make it if the correct time is what she thinks it is. Who misses the plane, and who makes it on time?

Daily Warm-Ups: Logic

© 2004 Walch Publishing

The Favorite Sports

There are four students named Becca, Felipe, Hilary, and Steven. Each has a favorite sport. These sports are basketball, fishing, hiking, and soccer, but not necessarily in the order of their names above. The following information is known about these students and their favorite sports:

1. No student's name begins with the same first letter as his or her favorite sport.

2. Felipe and Hilary like team sports.

3. Becca spent last summer vacationing at a lake, where she avoided hiking.

4. If Steven likes hiking, Felipe doesn't like basketball.

What is the favorite sport of each student?

126

© 2004 Walch Publishing

The Committee Elects a Chair

The school antipollution committee consists of five members. The members are Jenna, Khalid, Matt, Raoul, and Téa. At their first meeting they sit at a round table in the above order. They decide to elect a chairperson.

The first ballot is a standoff, with each member getting a single vote. No member has voted for either of his or her neighbors or for herself or himself. After some discussion, they decide to have a second ballot.

On the second ballot, all stick to their original choices except for Matt, who votes for Téa. Thus, Téa becomes the chairperson.

Who votes for Khalid on the first ballot?

© 2004 Walch Publishing

127

Competitors

Erin, Manuel, and Pablo are competing for the school chess team. They are the number one player, the number two player, and a new student who has just finished the first day of school and is trying out for the team. However, their positions are not necessarily in the order of the names above.

Arriving at the classroom late, the number one player asks the coach for permission to play the number two player. However, the coach says that the number two player is already competing with the new student. Curious about the new student, the number one player asks the coach for information. The coach replies with the following statements:

1. "The new student takes more risks in the game than you do."

2. "You are a bigger risk-taker than Erin."

3. "Pablo and Erin were here on time."

From the information provided, identify the names of the number one player, the number two player, and the new student.

128

© 2004 Walch Publishing

The Car Owners

Ms. Toyota, Ms. Honda, and Ms. Mazda own a Toyota, a Honda, and a Mazda, but not necessarily in that order. The following facts are known about the car owners:

1. The Honda owner often goes hiking with Ms. Mazda.

2. Ms. Mazda sometimes has lunch with the Toyota's owner.

3. Ms. Honda is much younger than the Honda's owner.

Which car does each woman own?

Daily Warm-Ups: Logic

129

© 2004 Walch Publishing

The Fastest

The school cross-country running coaches had the team members run a series of 40-yard sprints to determine the fastest members of the group. Those with the fastest times were Carlos, Jaime, John, Rian, and Will. In the final sprint among these five players, the coaches made the following observations:

1. Will was faster than Carlos and slower than John.

2. Jaime was slower than Rian.

3. John was faster than Will and slower than Jaime.

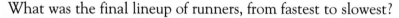

What was the final lineup of runners, from fastest to slowest?

130

© 2004 Walch Publishing

The Golfers and Their New Cars

Ms. Kaplan, Mr. Hall, Mr. Lee, and Ms. Silva play golf together every Saturday morning. Each has recently purchased a new car. Now they own a Subaru, a Fiat, a Mazda, and a Volvo, but not necessarily in the order of their names above. Consider the following statements:

Daily Warm-Ups: Logic

1. The owner of the Volvo beat both Mr. Hall and Ms. Silva during their last golf game.

2. Ms. Silva thinks that she is a better golfer than the owner of the Subaru or the owner of the Fiat.

3. Mr. Lee's car is not a Fiat or a Volvo.

What is the make of the car that each person owns?

131

© 2004 Walch Publishing

Getting Home for the Holiday Season

Three students, all who live in Chicago, attend an eastern university. They are going home for the holiday season. The names of the students are Rob, Liza, and Katya. One of the students goes by bus; one rides in a car with a friend; and one takes a plane. Three more facts about the students' rides home are:

1. The student who goes by plane is not Rob.

2. Katya and the student who goes by bus do not know each other.

3. Rob and the student who goes by bus are close friends.

How does each student get home for the holidays?

132

© 2004 Walch Publishing

The Finalists

The following students reached the finals of the conference wrestling tournament: Bay, Feldman, King, Lewis, Sanchez, Reeves, Liu, and Wagner. They were the finalists in the flyweight, lightweight, middleweight, and heavyweight divisions. During the finals, the following observations were made:

1. Sanchez lost the middleweight final by a pin, and Feldman defaulted in the flyweight final.

2. Bay weighed in as a flyweight, and Wagner was the heaviest winner of all.

3. King defeated Lewis, and Liu won by a pin.

Who were the champions and runners-up for each of the four divisions?

133

© 2004 Walch Publishing

The Lineup

Three advertising executives named Kim, Megan, and Shira have just finished working on an account. They are walking together, one behind the other, out of the office. Kim, the most creative of the three, always tells the truth. Megan sometimes tells the truth. Shira, the least creative of the group, never tells the truth.

A security officer in the lobby of their office building sees them leaving and asks them to identify themselves. The women respond as follows:

The woman in the middle says, "I'm Megan."

The woman in front says, "The woman in the middle is Kim."

The third woman says, "The woman in the middle is Shira."

Identify each person by name and the position in which she is walking.

Daily Warm-Ups: Logic

134

© 2004 Walch Publishing

First and Last Names

Two girls, Fiona and Shaquira, and two boys, Nate and Ty, are in the same English class. Their last names are Berg, Cho, Jones, and Wolinsky, but not necessarily in that order. From the statements below, match the first and last names of the students.

1. Nate's last name is not Berg or Jones.

2. Fiona's last name is not Berg or Cho.

3. Ty's last name is not Berg or Jones.

4. Nate's last name is shorter than Ty's.

135

© 2004 Walch Publishing

The Theft

One day at noon, as the vice principal of the high school was getting ready to go to lunch, she discovered that her bag was missing from her desk. Only four students had been in her office that morning, so she called them in for questioning. She knew that three of these students always told the truth, but one of them consistently lied. When questioned, the students made the following statements:

Ray: "Denise did it."

Denise: "Abby did it."

Zack: "I didn't do it."

Abby: "Denise lied when she said I did it."

How did the vice principal know which student was guilty?

136

© 2004 Walch Publishing

Comparing Semester Grades

Ella, Jack, and Vanno were comparing their semester grades for American history, English, and geometry. Each student received a grade of "A" for one subject, a grade of "B" for one subject, and a grade of "C" for one subject. Using the following clues, find the grades each student received for the three subjects:

1. No two students had the same grade for any one subject.

2. Ella's grade for English was lower than Jack's grade for American history, but higher than Vanno's grade for geometry.

Daily Warm-Ups: Logic

137

© 2004 Walch Publishing

A Choice of Dinners

Five friends ate dinner together. Two of them had steak, and three of them had chicken. Additional facts about the dinners are as follows:

1. Dawn and Alexa had different kinds of dinners.

2. Henry and Palwasha had the same kinds of dinners.

3. Palwasha and Dawn had different kinds of dinners.

4. The name of the fifth diner was Antonio.

     Name the friends who had steak and those who had chicken.

© 2004 Walch Publishing

Who Took the CD Player?

During a school lunch period, a portable CD player disappeared from a lunch table where a group of students had been seated. Immediately after lunch, the principal rounded up three suspects who were known to have seen the CD player. They all denied taking it. Each suspect was unable to make three consecutive statements without lying. With questioning, the principal obtained the following statements:

Brian: "I never saw the radio." "Leon took it." "I'm innocent."

Leon: "I didn't do it." "Everything that Brian said is a lie." "Carlos is not the guilty person."

Carlos: "Brian lied when he said that he had never seen the radio." "Leon lied when he said everything Brian said was a lie." "I didn't take it."

From the above statements, which of the suspects is guilty of taking the radio?

© 2004 Walch Publishing

The Foreign Language Teachers

A certain high school has three teachers in its foreign language department. The names of these teachers are Ms. Ribeiro, Mr. Tran, and Ms. Olsen. They teach French, Latin, and Spanish, but not necessarily in that order. There are also three students at this school who have the same last names as these teachers, even though none of them is related. The following facts about these people are known:

1. Ms. Ribeiro often went sailing with the French teacher last summer.

2. By tutoring at odd times during the summer, the Spanish teacher received an amount of money that was exactly one third as much as the earnings of one of the students, a close neighbor.

3. The student named Tran lives in a town eight kilometers from the school.

4. The student named Ribeiro earned exactly a thousand dollars working at a resort during the summer.

5. The student with the same name as the Spanish teacher lives near the school.

Which subject does each person teach?

140

© 2004 Walch Publishing

Students and Their Chosen Professions

Dan, Leah, Max, Nina, and Satia are freshman, sophomore, junior, senior, and graduate students in economics, education, medicine, ministry, and law, but not necessarily in that order. The following facts are known about the students:

1. Leah will become an intern next year.

2. Dan and the sophomore ministry student room together.

3. Nina is in a higher class than Dan.

4. The education student graduated from the same high school as Dan and Max.

5. Satia is in law school.

Identify the students according to profession and class in school (assuming no coed dorms).

141

© 2004 Walch Publishing

Daily Warm-Ups: Logic

Naming the Ships

A passenger ship, a tanker, and a cargo ship are named S. S. *Adams*, S. S. *Kennedy*, and S. S. *Monroe*, but not respectively. Their ports of departure and destinations are Boston, Charleston, London, Miami, New York, and Philadelphia, listed alphabetically. The following facts are known about the ships:

1. The S. S. *Kennedy* arrived in Boston on the same day the passenger ship left London.

2. The S. S. *Adams* left Philadelphia with a cargo of steel and did not go to New York, although one of the others did.

3. The tanker met the ship going to Miami.

What are the names of the cargo ship, the passenger ship, and the tanker, and what are their respective ports of departure and destinations?

142

© 2004 Walch Publishing

A Quiet Evening at Home

After finishing their school work, Mr. Nucci's four children are spending a quiet evening at home. They are sitting around the living room painting, writing, sorting photographs, and reading while listening to music on the CD player. The following facts are known about the children:

1. Natty is not writing or reading.

2. Laura isn't sorting photos or writing.

3. Joey is neither reading nor painting.

4. Denny does not like to write or paint.

5. If Laura is not reading, Natty is not sorting photos.

What is each of Mr. Nucci's four children doing?

143

© 2004 Walch Publishing

The Walkathon

Four couples, who are high-school seniors, will be participating in a walkathon for charity. The names of the young women are Cara, Michelle, Keisha, and Maddie. The names of the young men are Ben, Ramon, Mark, and Ahmed. The following facts are known about the couples:

1. Michelle isn't walking with Mark or Ben.

2. Maddie isn't walking with Ben or Ahmed.

3. Keisha isn't walking with Mark or Ben.

4. Ramon isn't walking with Michelle.

Match the couples who will be in the walkathon.

144

Daily Warm-Ups: Logic

© 2004 Walch Publishing

Who Does What?

The members of a household are Mr. Layton, his wife, their daughter, and Mr. Layton's father. One of the members is a chemist and another is a teacher. The following facts are known about the household members and their occupations:

1. If the chemist is a man, then the chemist and the teacher are not blood relatives.

2. If the teacher is a man, then the chemist is a man.

3. If the chemist and the teacher are blood relatives, the chemist is younger than the teacher.

4. If the teacher is not a man, then the chemist is not a man.

Which of the household members is the chemist and which is the teacher?

Daily Warm-Ups: Logic

145

© 2004 Walch Publishing

The Basketball Players

Five professional basketball players named Earl, Mahesh, Carlo, Joe, and Tyrone have hometowns of Bangor, Denver, Miami, Phoenix, and San Francisco, but not necessarily in that order. When they are asked by a sports reporter where they live, they list the names of their hometowns and then respond as follows:

1. Earl: "I live west of Mahesh, but Tyrone lives nearer to Carlo than I live."

2. Mahesh: "The state where I live starts with the same letter as the first letter in the word *candy*."

3. Carlo: "My home state borders on only one other state."

4. Joe: "I live east of Earl and north of Tyrone."

5. Tyrone: "The others have told where I live."

The reporter was able to connect each player with his hometown. Can you do as well?

146

The Creative Arts Students

Four young women named Kathleen, Hawa, Ming, and Teresa are majoring in creative arts in college. One is studying to be an actor, one an artist, one a dancer, and one a singer, but not necessarily in that order. The following additional information is known about these women:

Daily Warm-Ups: Logic

1. Both Hawa and the student who hopes to be an actor have sat for paintings by the student who hopes to become an artist.

2. The student who hopes to become an actor is the roommate of Teresa and sometimes has lunch with Kathleen.

3. Hawa has never seen Teresa.

4. Kathleen and Ming congratulated the student who hopes to become a singer on her performance at a concert.

Determine the college majors of each of the students.

147

© 2004 Walch Publishing

The Three Relatives

Three people—Jerry, Jess, and Kit—are related to one another. The following facts are known about these people:

1. Jerry's legal spouse and Jerry are opposite genders.

2. Jerry's legal spouse and Jess's sibling are the same gender.

3. Each of these three people is one of the following: Jerry's legal spouse, Jess's sibling, or Kit's brother-in-law.

Determine the gender of each of the three people, and tell how they are related to one another.

148

© 2004 Walch Publishing

Ages Listed in Order

Four people, whose names are Danil, Dennis, Dominica, and Dan, are discussing their ages. They are overheard making the following statements:

1. Dominica: "Dan, who is my older brother, has just celebrated his seventeenth birthday."

2. Danil: "I am older than Dan and younger than Dennis."

Assuming that both statements are true, list the names of the four people in order of their ages, starting with the oldest.

Daily Warm-Ups: Logic

149

© 2004 Walch Publishing

Passengers and Crew

On an airplane flying from Boston to Los Angeles, there are passengers named Clifford, Leon, and Testa. By some coincidence, the pilot, copilot, and navigator have the same first names as these passengers, but not necessarily in that order. Additional facts about these people are:

1. The passenger with the same name as the navigator lives in Los Angeles.

2. The passenger who lives nearest the navigator chews gum.

3. Testa, a member of the crew, recently beat the copilot at racquetball.

4. Passenger Clifford lives in Boston.

5. Passenger Leon thinks that chewing gum is vulgar.

6. The navigator lives halfway between Boston and Los Angeles.

Who are the pilot, copilot, and navigator?

© 2004 Walch Publishing

The Strawberry Pickers

During summer vacation Luis, Ellie, Tran, and Selina worked together picking strawberries. At the end of the season, they compared the amount of berries that each had picked. They made note of the following facts:

1. Ellie picked more than Luis and Tran picked together.

2. The total that Luis and Ellie picked equaled the total that Tran and Selina picked together.

3. The total picked by Luis and Selina was more than the total picked by Ellie and Tran.

Arrange the names of the berry pickers in the order of the amount of berries that each picked, starting with the person who picked the most.

151

© 2004 Walch Publishing

The Poisoned Coffee

After a business meeting at a restaurant, four executives finished their lunch with some coffee. One of them, who had just finished her coffee, suddenly struggled to her feet and cried out, "I've been poisoned!" She then fell over, dead.

All the companions of the dead woman were arrested. When questioned by the police, each suspect made three statements, two of which were true and one of which was false. The statements were as follows:

Ms. Mason: "I was sitting next to Ms. Berg." "We had our usual waiter today." "I didn't do it."

Ms. Hernandez: "The waiter didn't do it." "I was sitting across the table from Ms. Wright." "We had a new waiter today."

Ms. Berg: "Ms. Mason lied when she said we had our usual waiter." "Ms. Hernandez didn't do it." "The waiter poisoned Ms. Wright."

If only these three businesswomen and the waiter were involved in the crime, who poisoned Ms. Wright?

152

© 2004 Walch Publishing

The Junior Prom

Drew, Charlie, Jamal, and LeBron arranged to go to the junior prom together with their dates. Their dates are Becky, Keisha, Shira, and Lydia, but not necessarily in that order. The members of this group exchanged dances, and at one time during the prom, the following couples were seen dancing together:

1. Lydia was dancing with Becky's date.

2. Charlie was dancing with Jamal's date.

3. Becky was dancing with Shira's date.

4. Jamal was dancing with Drew's date.

5. Keisha was dancing with Drew.

The challenge is to resolve all of these mixed-up pairs and tell who went to the prom with whom.

153

© 2004 Walch Publishing

The Outstanding Characteristics of Four Friends

Allie, Grace, Elena, and Page are seniors in high school who are close friends. Each of these young women has two outstanding characteristics, but no two of them have the same two characteristics. Two of the girls are very artistic, two of them are skilled runners, two of them are strong in foreign languages, and two are keen scientists. The following additional facts are known about these students:

1. Page is very good at languages, but Allie is not.

2. Elena is very artistic, but Grace is not.

3. Grace is good at science, but Allie is not.

4. Allie is a fast runner, but Elena is not.

5. Elena does not have either of the characteristics of Grace.

What are the two outstanding characteristics of each student?

154

Who Took the Candy Bar?

During a sporting event at school, a group of five students from Ms. Antoniou's homeroom went to the snack bar. One of the five took a candy bar without paying for it. When the students were questioned by the school principal, they made these statements in the following order:

1. Octavius: "Neither Alex nor I did it."

2. Jack: "It was Octavius or Misha."

3. Misha: "Both Octavius and Jack are lying."

4. Dan: "Misha's statement about Octavius and Jack is not true; one of them is lying, and the other is speaking the truth."

5. Alex: "What Dan said is wrong."

When Ms. Antoniou was consulted, she said, "Three of these students are always truthful, but everything that two of them say will be a lie."

Assuming that their teacher is correct, can you determine who took the candy bar?

155

© 2004 Walch Publishing

The Men With Double Occupations

Mr. Chinn, Mr. Gates, and Mr. Reyes each have two different occupations. The six occupations are author, bookkeeper, cab driver, firefighter, gardener, and musician, but not necessarily in that order. Identify the two occupations of each person from the following statements:

1. Mr. Reyes hired the gardener to plant some trees.

2. Both the musician and the gardener go bowling with Mr. Chinn.

3. The firefighter is married to the author's sister.

4. The author asked the bookkeeper to help him prepare his income tax.

5. Mr. Gates is a better chess player than either Mr. Reyes or the author.

6. The firefighter and the musician often attend concerts together.

156

© 2004 Walch Publishing

The Highway Test

Five new car models were tested under highway conditions for acceleration and speed. They were a Ford, a Honda, a Volvo, a Toyota, and a Dodge. The following facts are known about the outcome:

1. The Honda finished one or two places after the Volvo.

2. The Toyota did not finish either one place before or one place after the Dodge.

3. The Volvo did not finish third.

4. The Dodge didn't finish either one place before or one place after the Honda.

5. The Dodge did not finish first or last.

Find the order in which the five cars finished the highway test.

157

© 2004 Walch Publishing

Staff Organization

The organization of a grocery store staff, during the morning shift, consists of the manager, assistant manager, cashier, bookkeeper, clerk, and bagger. The names of the personnel, in alphabetical order, are Ms. Britos, Mr. Brown, Mr. Campbell, Mr. DaSilva, Ms. Liu, and Ms. Womack. The following facts are known about these people:

1. Mr. Campbell is 25 years old; Mr. Brown is 26.

2. The cashier is the bookkeeper's son-in-law.

3. The bagger is Ms. Britos's stepsister.

4. Mr. DaSilva is the manager's neighbor.

5. The assistant manager is the grandson of the manager and the manager's husband (who does not work at the store).

6. Mr. Brown, Ms. Britos, and Ms. Womack are unmarried.

What position does each person hold in the store?

© 2004 Walch Publishing

Two Jobs Apiece

There are three people named Jesse, Dan, and Azad. Each of these people has two occupations. The jobs are hairstylist, writer, cook, gardener, musician, and painter, but not necessarily in that order. From the list of facts below, see if you can identify each person's occupations.

1. Dan owed the gardener some money.

2. The painter had an argument with the writer.

3. Azad beat both Dan and the painter at chess.

4. The cook offended the musician by laughing at his latest composition.

5. Both the musician and the gardener go biking with Jesse.

6. The cook invited the painter's sister to a movie.

159

© 2004 Walch Publishing

Planning Careers

Four high-school seniors are planning different careers. The names of the students are Carmen, Joe, Mary, and Gustav. One student plans to become a certified public accountant, one a lawyer, one a teacher, and one an enlisted member of the navy. Their surnames are Doyle, Fong, Perry, and Sanchez. Using the clues provided below, identify the full name and planned vocation of each student.

1. Gustav expects to engage in his chosen career immediately after his graduation from high school.

2. The student whose surname is Doyle, the student planning to be a certified public accountant, and Carmen all have the same English class.

3. The student whose surname is Doyle hopes to become the bride of the student whose surname is Sanchez.

4. Carmen does not plan to become a teacher.

5. The student whose surname is Fong won a varsity letter in boys' football.

6. Joe, who does not plan to become a teacher, is a good friend of the student whose surname is Sanchez.

160

The Three Musicians and Their Daughters

The names of three musicians are Ms. Ortiz, Ms. Lin, and Ms. Fox. One of the musicians plays a clarinet, another plays a flute, and the third plays a saxophone. Each is the mother of a high-school senior. The following additional facts are known about these musicians and their daughters:

1. The musician who plays the clarinet is 19 dm tall.

2. The younger Fox is 2 dm shorter than the younger Lin.

3. The saxophone player is 18 dm tall.

4. The flute player and the younger Lin are 20 dm tall.

5. The musician who plays the clarinet has exactly half as many CDs as the person in this group who is her same height.

6. The younger Ortiz's mother is more athletic than the flute player.

7. The daughter of the saxophone player has 225 orchestral CDs and 330 vocal CDs.

What is the name of the woman who plays the clarinet?

161

© 2004 Walch Publishing

A Dramatic Dinner Party

Emilio and Tessa invited Tucker and Mandy over for dinner at their new house. During a tour of the house, someone jostled another. The person who was jostled lost balance, fell down a flight of stairs, and died of a broken neck. From the following facts, identify the victim as well as the person who caused the accident.

1. Tessa played tennis regularly with one of the others.

2. Mandy was released from a hospital on the day of the accident, after having been confined there for two days.

3. Tucker had his injured leg in a cast for over a year.

4. Tucker met Emilio's mother only once.

5. Emilio will not expose his sibling's guilt.

6. The victim dined in a restaurant on the previous evening with the person who regularly played tennis with Tessa.

7. Mandy met Tessa only six days before the accident.

8. The hostess was asked to give information about the person who caused the accident.

162

© 2004 Walch Publishing

Naming the Football Officials

The officials assigned to cover an opening football game are Enzo, Juan, Jack, and Roy. They will serve as referee, umpire, head linesman, and field judge, but not necessarily in that order. Match the names of these people and their assignments based on the following information:

1. Only Enzo and Roy are married.

2. The field judge's wife is in the stands watching the game.

3. The referee does not wear glasses.

4. The head linesman wears glasses.

5. Juan and Enzo do not wear glasses.

6. The head linesman is engaged to be married.

7. Roy rode to the game with his neighbor, who is the umpire.

8. Jack and Roy may or may not wear glasses.

9. The referee and the umpire live in the same city; the others do not.

Daily Warm-Ups: Logic

© 2004 Walch Publishing

The Doctors

Denise, Maria, and Saira are the daughters of Dr. Alvarez, Dr. Kahn, and Dr. Reed, who are a professor, a dentist, and a physician, but not necessarily in that order. Use the statements below to match the parents to their professions and their daughters.

1. Dr. Kahn is not the physician.

2. Dr. Alvarez's daughter and Maria went swimming with the physician's daughter.

3. The best friends of the dentist's daughter are Denise and Maria.

164

© 2004 Walch Publishing

Three Students

Three college students, Colin, Gabe, and Reuben, are seniors at Midwestern University. Their home states are California, Georgia, and Rhode Island. One drives a Camry, one drives a GMC Suburban, and one drives a RAV4. The following additional information is known about the students:

1. None of the three students lives in a state or drives a car with a name that starts with the same letter as his first name.

2. The state where each student lives starts with a different letter than the car he drives.

3. Colin does not live in Georgia.

What is the home state of each student, and which car does he drive?

Daily Warm-Ups: Logic

165

© 2004 Walch Publishing

A Social-Studies Project

Three students, whose first names are Brian, Emily, and Marisa, are working together on a social-studies project. One student is doing interviews, one is doing editing and writing, and one is doing Internet research. Their surnames are Cox, Jankowitz, and Wong, but not necessarily in that order. The following statements are true about these students:

1. Emily's surname is not Cox.

2. The student whose surname is Wong and the girl who is doing the Internet research are neighbors.

3. Brian is not doing the interviews.

4. The student whose surname is Jankowitz likes to go fishing with his father.

What is each student's full name, and what part of the social-studies project is each working on?

166

© 2004 Walch Publishing

The Tennis Players

Four high-school students enjoy playing tennis together. Two of the students are female and two are male. The first names of the girls are Mary Lou and Tanya; the first names of the boys are Nando and David. The surnames of the students are Chinn, Hayes, Freitas, and Kyros. The following statements are true about these students:

1. The student whose surname is Freitas has a much better serve than the young woman whose surname is Kyros.

2. Mary Lou and Tanya often play doubles against Nando and the freshman boy.

3. The student whose surname is Chinn is in a class above Tanya and a class below Mary Lou.

4. The student whose surname is Hayes is a senior.

Identify each student's full name and high-school class.

Who Owns the Speedboats?

The Bishop family has a speedboat, and so has each of their four closest family friends, the LaCasses, the Zilkhas, the Laytons, and the Parks. All of these families enjoy spending time at the lake where they berth their boats. Each family has one daughter, and each has named their boat after a daughter of one of their close friends. Consider these facts about the families, their boats, and their daughters:

1. There is a speedboat named *Greta*.

2. *Julia*, owned by the LaCasses, is named after the Laytons' daughter.

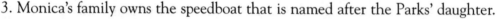

3. Monica's family owns the speedboat that is named after the Parks' daughter.

4. The Bishops own *Molly*.

5. The Laytons' speedboat is *Monica*.

6. The Zilkhas own *Anisa*.

Which family owns which boat, and what is each girl's full name?

168

© 2004 Walch Publishing

College Students and Their Home States

The first names of four college students are Ahmed, David, Kate, and Rosa. Their surnames are Evans, Gomez, Rashid, and Peterson, but not necessarily in that order. The homes of the students are in Kentucky, Michigan, Ohio, and Wisconsin, but not necessarily in that order. Here are some facts about the students:

1. The young woman whose surname is Peterson has never gone bowling.

2. The student whose surname is Gomez and the student from Ohio are in the same Spanish class.

3. Ahmed is not from Kentucky.

4. The student whose surname is Evans, the student from Ohio, and Kate go bowling together.

5. The student from Michigan sometimes has his lunch with Ahmed.

6. Rosa's surname is not Evans.

7. The young woman from Wisconsin often plays tennis with Rosa.

Identify the full name and home state of each student.

169

© 2004 Walch Publishing

A School Assembly Committee

Nine students were selected by the student body to plan an assembly program. These students met and elected a chairperson. After the meeting, they were heard making these statements:

Ali: "Emma is the chairperson."

Becca: "Ali is not telling the truth."

Charlie: "I am the chairperson."

Dan: "It is either Charlie or Hamdi."

Emma: "You should not believe Becca."

Felipe: "Charlie is telling the truth."

Gabe: "Felipe is lying."

Hamdi: "Felipe is not telling the truth, but I'm not the chairperson."

Imani: "Ali is wrong, but Hamdi is right."

If only three of the above statements are correct, who is the committee chairperson?

Daily Warm-Ups: Logic

© 2004 Walch Publishing

Walking Partway Home

Jenna attends a college in a town some distance from her home. Every Friday during the school year, her mother meets her at the local bus station and drives her home for the weekend. One Friday, Janet arrives at the bus station a half hour early. She begins to walk home along the route her mother always takes to meet her. As expected, her mother meets her en route and takes her the rest of the way home. Had Janet waited at the bus station, her mother would have picked her up exactly on time. In this case, however, Janet reaches home ten minutes early.

For how long does Janet walk?

Daily Warm-Ups: Logic

© 2004 Walch Publishing

Playing Monopoly®

As part of their study of the nation's monetary system, four economics students are playing Monopoly. Their names are Beth, Sophie, Josh, and Karim. They are listed in the teacher's record book after the numbers 3, 6, 11, and 16, but not necessarily in that order. The following observations are made at one time during the game:

1. One student has fifteen houses on his or her properties.

2. The student with the smallest number in the teacher's record book doesn't have fifteen houses.

3. Beth plays before Karim.

4. Josh is number 6 in the teacher's record book, and he doesn't have fifteen houses.

5. Karim's name goes after the student with fifteen houses.

172

6. The student whose number is 3 in the teacher's record book plays after the student whose number is 11 and before the student whose number is 6.

7. Sophie plays after Karim, but before Josh.

Indicate the order in which the students play and give their numbers in their teacher's record book.

© 2004 Walch Publishing

Daily Warm-Ups: Logic

The Tradesmen

Mr. Glazier, Mr. Locksmith, Mr. Painter, and Mr. Plumber are, among them, a glazier, a locksmith, a painter, and a plumber. Each man has a grown son and daughter. The sons are also, among them, a glazier, a locksmith, a painter, and a plumber. No man, father or son, has the trade suggested by his name. Furthermore, no son has the trade of his father. Each of the sons is married to the sister of another son. None of the married sisters has a husband or a father-in-law with the trade suggested by her birth name. The following additional facts are known:

1. The plumber's son married Ms. Painter.

2. The trade of Mr. Locksmith Sr. is the same as the birth name of the young woman who married Mr. Painter's son.

3. Each young woman changed her surname when she married, and that surname had a different first initial from her birth name.

What is the trade of each father, what is the trade of each son, and which daughter did each son marry?

173

© 2004 Walch Publishing

Finding the Correct Answers to a Test

Four students were not paying attention during a class lesson. The teacher asked these students to report after school for a makeup assignment. When the students arrived after school, the teacher gave them a short test on the lesson that day, promising that they would not have to do any further work if they answered all of the questions correctly. The test consisted of four questions. In the chart below are the names of the students and the answers they gave on the test.

	Question 1	Question 2	Question 3	Question 4
Jade	France	Italy	Germany	England
Charles	Germany	Italy	France	England
Jessie	France	England	Italy	Germany
Leon	England	France	Germany	Italy

174

When the students had all finished the test, they asked the teacher how they had done. "Not so well," the teacher responded. "One of you had them all wrong, while three of you each had two right."

What are the correct answers to questions 1, 2, 3, and 4?

© 2004 Walch Publishing

The Teacher Problem

The surnames of five teachers are Alameda, Berkeley, Hayward, Oakland, and Piedmont. Each of these teachers lives in a city that is the namesake of one of the other teachers. Unusual as it may seem, each of the teachers works in a second city that is the name of one of the others. No two of the teachers either live or teach in the same city. Following are additional facts about the teachers, where they live, and where they teach:

1. The teacher named Oakland teaches in Piedmont.

2. The teacher who lives in Alameda works in Oakland.

3. The teacher who lives in Piedmont works in the city that is the namesake of the teacher who lives in Alameda.

4. The teacher named Berkeley teaches in the city that is the namesake of the teacher who lives in Piedmont.

What is the surname of the teacher who teaches in Berkeley?

175

© 2004 Walch Publishing

Home Cities and Occupations

Five people, who were close friends in high school, are attending a class reunion. They are Ms. Day, Mr. Evans, Mr. Louis, Ms. Pitt, and Mr. Traverse. Their occupations are doctor, engineer, lawyer, plumber, and teacher. By coincidence, they live in the cities of Dayton, Evansville, Louisville, Pittsburg, and Traverse City, but no one lives in the city with the name similar to his or hers. No person's occupation begins with the same letter as his or her name *or* the name of the city in which he or she lives. In addition, the following facts are known:

1. Ms. Pitt lives in Traverse City and is neither a lawyer nor an engineer.

2. Ms. Day is not a resident of Evansville, nor is Mr. Traverse, who is not a lawyer or a doctor.

3. Mr. Evans is neither a lawyer nor a doctor, nor does he live in Louisville or Pittsburg.

4. The teacher does not live in Dayton.

Name the occupation of each person and the city in which he or she lives.

176

© 2004 Walch Publishing

Three Students and Their Teachers

Three high-school students, whose surnames are Antonio, Bell, and Chatterjee, usually walk to school together. When they arrive at school, they go to different first-period classes—one to English, one to history, and one to math. One of the students is a sophomore, one is a junior, and one is a senior. Three teachers with the same surnames as the students teach the three subjects the students take. One of the teachers is a young woman, one is an older woman, and one is a middle-aged man. Using the clues provided below, identify the first-period class that each student attends, the high-school class of each student, and the subject taught by each teacher.

1. No student attends a class taught by a teacher with the same surname.

2. The senior student has the same surname as the English teacher.

3. Student Chatterjee does not attend the English class or the class taught by the man with the surname of Bell.

4. The math student is not the sophomore.

5. The young female teacher does not teach the subject attended by the senior.

6. Student Antonio does not go to the history class or the English class.

177

© 2004 Walch Publishing

A Basketball Tournament

Four high-school basketball teams played in the semifinals of a basketball tournament. The teams were Jefferson, Kennedy, Lincoln, and Washington. The team jerseys were blue, green, orange, and red, but not necessarily in that order. The names of the team captains were Jermaine, Earl, Enrique, and Rob.

Earl's team did not play Washington. In the final game of the tournament, Jermaine's team failed to score in the overtime period, and they missed two foul shots that could have won the game. Earl's team defeated Kennedy by four points. Jermaine did not see his cousin, the captain of the green team, play. Rob's team lost to the undefeated team. The red team lost to Lincoln in the initial game of the semifinals. The captain of the orange team saved his team from defeat by making a foul shot, just as the final buzzer sounded.

1. Which teams played each other in the semifinals and the finals?

2. What was the color of the jersey worn by each team?

3. Who was the captain of each team?

4. What was the margin of victory or defeat in each game?

© 2004 Walch Publishing

A Game of Chips

Jamal and Maria are playing a game with six chips arranged in three piles. The first pile contains one chip, the second pile contains two chips, and the third pile contains three chips. The players alternate plays and must take one, two, or three chips from only one pile per play. The player who takes the last chip is the loser.

If Jamal has the first play, how can he plan his plays to assure a win?

179

© 2004 Walch Publishing

Number Game

Two players take turns writing numbers from 1 through 10 on a sheet of paper. The player who writes the final number that brings the total up to 100 is the winner. The first player writes any number from 1 through 10; the second player crosses out this number and adds to it any number from 1 through 10, and so on until exactly 100 is reached. The player who writes 100 wins.

A clever player who discovers the secret to the game can win consistently. Can you figure out this secret?

180

© 2004 Walch Publishing

1. February 29
2. It is your left elbow; grasp it with your right hand.
3. Thursday
4. In
5. Cross out the *s* in *seven*.
6. *bookkeeper*
7. Mt. Everest
8. The bottle is worth 50¢.
9. She slept during the five nights.
10. Jason was either 2 kilometers south of the North Pole or 2 kilometers north of the South Pole.
11. 6
12. All months but February have thirty days (and seven months have thirty-one).
13. one hour
14. He made the apples into applesauce.
15. She has one quarter and three dimes.
16. Since two pounds of $10 gold pieces contain twice as much gold as a pound of $20 gold pieces, they are worth twice as much.

17. He lived for fifty-nine years; there is no year zero.
18. Measure the thickness of 200 pages in the book. Then divide by 100 to find the thickness of one sheet.
19. It rains.
20. Any animal can jump that high or higher; a house can't jump.
21. It wasn't raining.
22. when it gets to the bottom
23. wet
24. baby goats
25. a hole
26. water
27. carpet
28. an echo
29. Answers will vary. Possible answers include: silence, a promise, trust.
30. a shadow
31. 15¢
32. They talk the least in February; it's the shortest month.

Daily Warm-Ups: Logic

33. Tomas's grandfather is his mother's father, not his father's father.

34. This is because when you find it, you stop looking.

35.

36.

37.

38.

39.

40.

41.

42.

43.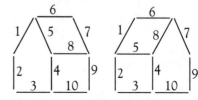

44. a hole in the ground
45. the letter *m*
46. four boys and three girls
47. fire
48. She will be away for nineteen days.
49. Jerry is Tom's grandfather.
50. Before a man can have a widow, he must be dead.
51. mother and son
52. Although it is a bit unusual, it is possible. Either Luis's mother or father has a sister the same age as Luis.
53. A man is speaking of himself.
54. One sister is the boy's aunt; the other is his mother. Alternatively, the boy could be the son of the first sister's brother-in-law or sister-in-law.
55. The son is half-brother to the sisters; the daughters are stepsisters.
56. The mother of the young man and his sister has a brother, who is the father of the woman in the picture. The woman in the picture is, therefore, a first cousin of the brother and sister.
57. The man is either the son or the nephew of the subject of the portrait.
58. Let's say that there are two girls, a boy, their father, their mother or stepmother, and their father's father and stepmother. After the grandfather's son is born, the grandfather remarries. The grandfather's son has one daughter and one son by a current marriage and one daughter by a former marriage.
59. The performer simply crossed her closed hands; the money, therefore, changed places.
60. They could have placed three pieces of candy in one dish and seven pieces in another, then taken one of these dishes and placed it, together with the candy, in the third dish.
61. She took a pair of scissors and neatly cut off one of the corners of the sheet of paper. When she counted the corners again, there were five. One more cut would provide six corners, and so on.
62. He removed a pencil from his coat pocket, extended part of it *through the small hole* in the paper, and with the pencil gently pushed the hat.
63. He wrote *ONE WORD*.

64. Pick up the second glass and pour its contents into the fifth glass; then return the second glass to its original position (count glasses from left to right).

65. She added the top sides of the dice, which she could see, and subtracted the total from 28. The difference would be the sum of the bottom sides of the dice. Instead of using 4 dice, she could have used 5 or 6; since the sum of the opposite sides is always 7, the sums of the top and bottom sides of 5 and 6 dice would be 35 and 42, respectively.

66. Cross out all three 9s, one of the ls, and two of the 7s. This leaves 11 and 7; their sum is 18.

67. It is not possible for an original coin to be dated B.C.E.

68. Polar bears are native to the Arctic regions; penguins are native to the Antarctic regions.

69. Anna knew that if the substance would quickly dissolve any substance it touched, it would have dissolved the glass vial that Cho was carrying.

70. She threw the ball straight up in the air.

71. Talia has $7 and Erin has $5.

72. Go to bed in the daytime.

73. He can put an odd number of horses in each of two fields and none in the third.

74. They will never be covered; a ship rises with the tide.

75. No. In seventy-two hours it will be midnight.

76. Perhaps the first thing to do is to get a straight edge (the edge of a sheet of paper will do) and determine which line is extended. Measuring is the only accurate way to verify distances and the positions of the lines. Sometimes we can't believe what we see.

77. They were facing each other.

78. He had four: a horse, a cow, a pig, and a goat.

79. The neighbor across the road had more land.

80. One tank has neither more nor less alcohol than the other has gasoline; the amounts are the same.

81. The word is *wrong*.

82. There were three people, not four, dividing the oranges: father, son, and grandson. Together, they made two fathers and two sons.

83. The young men had seen each other's face, and each naturally assumed that his face resembled the other's.

84. The doctor was Jaime's mother.
85. Statements 1, 2, 3, and 5 are false; statement 4 is true.
86. The burglar entered through the apartment door. Jamal *examined* the lock on the door, but he didn't lock it. The burglar was more thoughtful; he locked the door when he left.
87. The clock that didn't run at all was correct twice a day, at the time shown by the stopped hands. The other clock was correct only twice each year.
88. The girls were two members of a set of triplets, or quadruplets, etc.
89. Since Paul said that he walked home from the doctor's office, his parents knew he hadn't broken a leg. Since they also knew which hand Paul usually wrote with, they could determine that this was not the arm that he had broken, because he was able to write the letter.
90. The monkey and the weight will remain opposite each other. Since the two are perfectly balanced, the climbing monkey will not rise above or sink below the height of the weight.

91. The bookworm will eat through the cover of volume I plus volumes II, III, and IV, along with the cover of volume V, a distance of 15 centimeters (excluding the thickness of the first page and front cover of volume I and the last page and back cover of volume V).
92. The man first takes the goat across, leaving the wolf and the carrots. He then comes back and gets the wolf, which he takes to the other side, returning with the goat. Next, he leaves the goat and takes the carrots to the other side. Finally he comes back and gets the goat.
93. Two prisoners crossed the river; one remained on the far side while the other returned. Again, two prisoners crossed the river and one returned. Then two soldiers crossed the river; one prisoner and one soldier returned. Next, two soldiers crossed; one soldier returned, making two more trips across with the other two prisoners.
94. At the passing point, the two planes will be the same distance from Detroit (to the nearest kilometer, of course!).

95. Yes. A point on the earth's surface will be closer to the sun at true noon than at any other time during the day. At sunset, a point on the earth's surface in the tropical latitudes will be a distance approximately equal to the radius of the earth further from the sun than it was at noon. This added distance would be approximately 6,000 kilometers.

96. *"Where* on earth . . ?" would be a better question. The South Pole is the most logical answer.

97. Since you are standing on the International Date Line, as well as at the North Pole, part of you will be standing in the area where it is Monday and part of you will be standing in the area where it is Tuesday.

98. Yes, if the house were located directly over the South Pole.

99. The conditions of this story could only be satisfied at the North Pole. The bears in this region are polar bears, which are white. (There are no bears in the South Polar region.)

100. There is no missing dollar. The combined sales of a given number of candy bars at the rates of two for $1 and three for $1 is not the same as the rate of five for $2; it would actually be at the rate of twelve for $5.

101. He could first fill the 4-liter jar from the well. He could then fill the 3-liter jar from the 4-liter jar, leaving 1 liter of water in the 4-liter jar. Next, he could empty the 3-liter jar and pour the 1 liter of water from the 4-liter jar into it. Finally, he could fill the 4-liter jar. This would give him the 5 liters of water he needs.

102. They will first fill the 5-liter jar, then fill the 3-liter jar from it. This will leave 2 liters in the 5-liter jar. Next, they will empty the 3-liter jar back into the juice jug. Then they will pour the 2 liters from the 5-liter jar into the 3-liter jar. After filling the 5-liter jar again from the jug, they will finish filling the 3-liter jar from the 5-liter jar. This will leave 4 liters in the 5-liter jar, or half the juice.

103. She needs to take only three socks out to be sure of a matching pair.

104. The "missing" $8 is a matter of faulty bookkeeping presented in the puzzle. The hotel manager received $240 from the three journalists. She kept $200, her son kept $16, and the guests were returned a total of $24; this accounts for all of the money.

105. The two boys pedal to the doctor's office; one boy remains there, and the other comes back home for the father. The father then pedals to the doctor's office and sends the boy there back home to get the other boy.

106. The statements are not logical. Both the second and third statements contradict themselves. The word *never*, in the first statement, may create the dilemma; until human beings have reached a perfect state of being, liars will sometimes tell the truth, and truth-tellers will sometimes lie.

107. Turn glasses 1 and 2, then glasses 1 and 3, and finally glasses 2 and 3 (or glasses 1 and 3, then 1 and 2, and finally 1 and 2; or 1 and 2, then 1 and 2, and finally 1 and 3). All will then be upright. However, if you start by having the center glass with the top down and the other two glasses upright, the problem cannot be solved.

108. Sally asked, "Did your twin come with you this evening?" If the response was *yes*, she would know that the visitor was not telling the truth; if the response was *no*, she would know that the visitor was her boyfriend.

109. Since you know that each basket of fruit is incorrectly labeled, you should pick your piece of fruit from the basket marked *Oranges and Grapefruit*. If you take a grapefruit, then label the basket *Grapefruit*. You then know that the basket that was marked *Grapefruit* is incorrect, so it must be labeled as *Oranges* or *Oranges and Grapefruit*. However, since the basket labeled *Oranges* is also incorrect, that one should be relabeled as *Oranges and Grapefruit*. The remaining basket should be labeled *Oranges*. If you pick an orange, then the converse is true.

110. Ask the man, "Do you alternate true and false statements?" twice. Two *No* answers indicate that he always tells the truth; two *Yes* answers indicate

that he never tells the truth; and if he answers first *Yes* and then *No*, or first *No* and then *Yes*, he alternates true and false statements.

111. The adviser drew one of the pieces of paper out of the hat and tore it up, while announcing that it said *LIFE*. Since the remaining piece of paper said *DEATH*, the magistrate had to assume that the adviser had, indeed, drawn a piece of paper that said *LIFE* and was spared.

112. The first man to speak must have said, "I am a Waho," because if he were one, he would have told the truth. If he were not a Waho, he would have had to lie. The second man to speak must actually have been a Waho, because he quoted the first man correctly; since he said that the first man was a Waho, this had to be the truth. The third man to speak must have lied; since the second man was really a Waho, the third man had to be a Tabo. Thus, the first and second men were Wahos, and the third man was a Tabo.

113. The traveler said, "I will die by fire." He knew that if he were, indeed, to be roasted alive (by fire) his statement would be true, in which case (according to the king) he would have to be beheaded. However, if he were beheaded, that would make his statement false. Since his statement was neither true nor false, the king was forced to free the traveler. (The traveler was fortunate that the king kept his word!)

114. Two of the lawyers were women; the third lawyer was a man ("He"), and this was Johnson.

115. Let the first person propose a three-way division of the cake. Let the second person choose to redivide the cake or leave it. Then let the third person choose to redivide the cake or leave it. The first person to divide the cake can then choose a piece, and the other two should proceed in the "old" way (one of the two people who are to share the remaining parts redivide it into two portions; the other has the choice of portions).

116. Leah doesn't play lacrosse, so she must kayak and play tennis. Since Leah doesn't play lacrosse, Clara and Nikki must both play lacrosse. Since Nikki plays tennis, her games are tennis and

lacrosse. Clara's games are lacrosse and kayaking.
Summary: Leah—tennis and kayaking; Nikki—tennis and lacrosse; Clara—lacrosse and kayaking

117. Hannah and Anisa are women's names; Ben and Owen are men's names. Hannah is not Sportsgirl or Rockster, so she must be Anonymous or Animefan. Ben is not Sportsgirl and, since he doesn't like anime, probably isn't Animefan. Owen is not Anonymous or Rockster, so he is either Sportsgirl or Animefan. However, since Sportsgirl is probably a woman's screen name, Owen's screen name must be Animefan. If Owen's screen name is Animefan, then Hannah's screen name is Anonymous. It follows that Anisa's nickname is Sportsgirl and Ben's nickname is Rockster.
Summary: Hannah is Anonymous; Ben is Rockster; Owen is Animefan; Anisa is Sportsgirl.

118. According to statement 1, Hamdi is in a class below Chelsea, and Chelsea is in a class below Luisa. According to statement 2, Luisa is in a class below Josh.

Summary: Hamdi is a freshman; Chelsea is a sophomore; Luisa is a junior; Josh is a senior.

119. Neither Talia nor Ashley is the center, so Li must be the center. Talia is not the forward, and she is not the center, so she must be the guard. By elimination, Ashley is the forward.
Summary: Li—center; Talia—guard; Ashley—forward

120. Ms. Chang is not the counselor, Mr. Pejcek is not the principal, and Ms. Taylor is not the teacher. Mr. Pejcek is also not the counselor, so he must be the teacher. Since Ms. Chang is not the teacher, she must be the principal. By elimination, Ms. Taylor is the counselor.
Summary: Ms. Chang—principal; Mr. Pejcek—teacher; Ms. Taylor—counselor

121. Ramon did not have the toasted cheese sandwich or the fajita, so he must have had the veggie burger. Juanita didn't have the toasted cheese sandwich, and since Ramon had the veggie burger, she must have had the fajita. By

elimination, Hosea had the toasted cheese sandwich.

Summary: Ramon—veggie burger; Juanita—fajita; Hosea—toasted cheese sandwich

122. There are four possible true-false combinations of the two statements: TT, TF, FT, and FF. The first (TT) is eliminated, because we are told that at least one statement is false. The second (TF) and the third (FT) are eliminated, because in each case, if one person lied, the other cannot have spoken truthfully. Thus, both lied. The girl is therefore the person with black hair, and the boy is the person with blond hair.

123. It is easy to plot the runners on a line segment. Sara was the winner, Aileen and Midori were running second and third, Alyssa was fourth, Kate was fifth, and Imani was last.

124. Serena and Nick are sister and brother. Since Kai is Serena's nephew, but not Nick's nephew, he must be Nick's son.

125. Both the imagined and the real times can be plotted on a time line. Rachel and Alicia should reach the plane 15 minutes early; Ari will be 20 minutes late, and Emily will be 15 minutes late. Ari and Emily will miss the plane; Rachel and Alicia will be there on time.

Note: Numbers in parentheses in the answer solutions that follow indicate the relevant numbered statement in the logic problem itself.

126. Statement 1 means that Becca's favorite sport is not basketball; Felipe's is not fishing, Hilary's is not hiking, and Steven's is not soccer. If Felipe and Hilary like team sports (2), then Becca and Steven must like fishing and hiking. Becca's favorite sport must be fishing (3) since she avoids hiking, so Steven's favorite sport is hiking. Since Steven does like hiking, then Felipe must not like basketball (4) and therefore must like soccer. By elimination, Hilary's favorite sport is basketball.

Summary: Becca—fishing; Felipe—soccer; Hilary—basketball; Steven—hiking

127. Matt could vote for Jenna or Téa; on the first ballot, he must have voted for Jenna. Raoul could vote for Khalid or Jenna; since Matt voted for

Jenna, however, then Raoul must have voted for Khalid. So it was Raoul who voted for Khalid on the first ballot.

128. The number one player is not Pablo (3) and not Erin (3); Manuel is the number one player. Erin is not the new student, since she is less of a risk-taker than Manuel (2) and the new student is more of a risk-taker than Manuel (1); Erin must therefore be the number two player, and, by elimination, Pablo is the new student.
Summary: Manuel—number one player; Erin—number two player; Pablo—the new student

129. Ms. Mazda doesn't own the Honda (1), and she doesn't own the Toyota, so she must own the Mazda. Ms. Honda doesn't own the Honda (3), and since she can't own the Mazda, she must own the Toyota. This leaves Ms. Toyota as the owner of the Honda.
Summary: Ms. Mazda owns the Mazda; Ms. Honda owns the Toyota; Ms. Toyota owns the Honda.

130. Will was faster than Carlos, and John was faster than Will (1). Rian was faster than Jaime (2); Jaime was faster than Will (3) and John (3). When the positions are plotted on a speed line, the order is Rian, Jaime, John, Will, and Carlos.

131. Ms. Silva is not the owner of the Subaru or the Fiat (2). She is also not the owner of the Volvo (1), so she must own the Mazda. Mr. Lee's car is not a Fiat or a Volvo (3), nor is it a Mazda (Ms. Silva's car), so it must be a Subaru. Mr. Hall's car is not a Volvo (1), not a Mazda (Ms. Silva's car), and not a Subaru (Mr. Lee's car), so it must be a Fiat. By elimination, Ms. Kaplan's car is a Volvo.
Summary: Ms. Kaplan—Volvo; Mr. Hall—Fiat; Mr. Lee—Subaru; Ms. Silva—Mazda

132. Rob does not go by plane (1), and he does not go by bus (3), so he must go by car. Since Katya does not go by car (Rob does), and she doesn't go by bus (2), she must go by plane. This means that Liza goes by bus.
Summary: Rob—car; Liza—bus; Katya—plane

133. Sanchez was the middleweight runner-up (1). Feldman was the flyweight runner-up (1). Bay was

the flyweight winner (1, 2). Wagner was the heavyweight winner (2). King and Lewis must be lightweights, with King the winner (3). This leaves Liu as the middleweight winner and Reeves as the heavyweight runner-up.

Summary: Flyweight—Bay over Feldman; lightweight—King over Lewis; middleweight—Liu over Sanchez; heavyweight—Wagner over Reeves

134. The woman in the middle who identifies herself as Megan must not be telling the truth, since the two other women claim that the woman in the middle is someone different. Therefore, Megan must be either first or last in line. The woman who identifies the person in the middle as Kim is not telling the truth. The third woman must therefore be Kim. She says that Shira is in the middle, so Megan is first.

Summary: Megan is first; Shira is in the middle; Kim is last.

135. Since Fiona's, Nate's, and Ty's last names are not Berg (1, 2, 3), then Shaquira's last name is Berg. Since the last name of Nate and Ty is not Jones (1, 3), and Shaquira's last name is Berg, then Fiona's last name is Jones. Since Nate's last name is shorter than Ty's (4), his name must be Cho. By elimination, Ty's last name is Wolinsky.

Summary: Shaquira Berg; Nate Cho; Fiona Jones; Ty Wolinsky

136. Since only one of the four is guilty, than either Ray or Denise is lying. Since Zack and Abby must be telling the truth, then Denise is lying and is guilty.

137. Jack must have had a grade of "A" for American history; Ella must have had a grade of "B" for English; and Vanno must have had a grade of "C" for geometry (2). Ella couldn't have a grade of "A" for American history, since Jack had a grade of "A" for that subject (1), so her grade of "A" was for geometry; she had a grade of "C" for American history. Similarly, Jack had a grade of "B" for geometry and a grade of "C" for English. Vanno had a grade of "A" for English and a grade of "B" for American history.

Summary: Ella—"C" in American history, "B" in

English, and "A" in geometry; Jack—"A" in American history, "C" in English, and "B" in geometry; Vanno—"B" in American history, "A" in English, and "C" in geometry

138. Henry and Dawn had different types of dinners (2, 3). Henry, Palwasha, and Alexa had the same type of dinners (1, 2). Thus, Antonio and Dawn had steak; Henry, Palwasha, and Alexa had chicken.

139. Brian is not guilty, because if he were, all of Leon's statements would be true. Leon is not guilty, because if he were, all of Carlos's statements would be true. Carlos took the radio.

140. Mr. Tran is not the Spanish teacher, since the student named Tran lives far from school, yet the student with the same name as the Spanish teacher lives near the school (3, 5). The Spanish teacher's name is not Ms. Ribeiro, since the student named Ribeiro earned exactly $1,000, and the teacher would have had to receive exactly $333.33 $\frac{1}{3}$, which is not possible (2, 4). This leaves Ms. Olsen as the Spanish teacher. Ms. Ribeiro is not the French teacher (1), so she must be the

Latin teacher; Mr. Tran must be the French teacher. **Summary:** Ms. Ribeiro—Latin teacher; Mr. Tran—French teacher; Ms. Olsen—Spanish teacher

141. Satia is the graduate law student (5). Max is the sophomore ministry student (2). Leah is the senior medical student (1). Dan is the freshman (2, 3), but not the education student (4); he is studying economics. This leaves Nina as the junior education student.

Summary: Dan—freshman, economics; Leah—senior, medicine; Max—sophomore, ministry; Nina—junior, education; Satia—graduate, law

142. Since the S. S. *Kennedy* is neither the passenger ship that leaves London nor the cargo ship (which is the S. S. *Adams*), the S. S. *Kennedy* must be the tanker. The name of the passenger ship is therefore S. S. *Monroe*. If the tanker (S. S. *Kennedy*) met the ship going to Miami, and if the *Kennedy*'s destination was Boston, then its port of departure must have been Charleston. This means that the S. S. *Monroe* goes to New York from London,

and that the S. S. *Adams* is the ship heading to Miami (from Philadelphia).

Summary: S. S. *Adams*—cargo ship, Philadelphia to Miami; S. S. *Kennedy*—tanker, Charleston to Boston; S. S. *Monroe*—passenger ship, London to New York

143. Joey and Denny are not painting (3, 4); Natty, Laura, and Denny are not writing (1, 2, 3); Laura is not sorting photos, and Natty and Joey are not reading (1, 3). From statement 5, if Laura is not reading, she is painting, and Natty is painting, too; since this is not possible, Laura must be reading. Since Laura is reading, then Denny must be sorting photos. It follows that Joey is writing and Natty is painting.

Summary: Laura is reading; Denny is sorting photos; Joey is writing; Natty is painting.

144. Michelle doesn't walk with Ben, Mark, or Ramon (1, 4); therefore, she must walk with Ahmed. Keisha doesn't walk with Ben or Mark (3), and she doesn't walk with Ahmed (who's walking with Michelle), so she walks with Ramon. Maddie doesn't go with Ben (2), Ahmed, or Ramon, so she walks with Mark. Thus, Cara walks with Ben.

Summary: Cara goes with Ben; Keisha goes with Ramon; Michelle goes with Ahmed; Maddie goes with Mark.

145. Since the two men are blood relatives, and one of the men (Mr. Layton's father) and the wife are not, and since statement 2 would be a contradiction to statement 1, the chemist must be a woman. Statement 4 states that since the chemist is a woman, the teacher is also a woman. Since the two women are blood relatives, the daughter must be the chemist (who is younger), and Mr. Layton's wife must be the teacher.

146. (Use a map of the United States as students solve this problem.) We can assume that the states in question are Maine, Colorado, Florida, Arizona, and California, since these are major cities in these states. Of these five states, Maine is the only one that borders only one other state, so Carlo must be from Bangor (3). Mahesh lives in either Colorado or California (both begin with a C).

However, he must live in Colorado, since he lives nearer to Tyrone than Earl. Earl lives west of Mahesh (4), and Joe lives east of Earl (4). Thus, Mahesh lives in Denver. Tyrone lives closer to Carlo than Earl and south of Joe, so he must live in Miami. Since Joe lives east of Earl, he must live in Phoenix. This leaves Earl living in San Francisco.

Summary: Earl lives in San Francisco; Mahesh lives in Denver; Carlo lives in Bangor; Joe lives in Phoenix; Tyrone lives in Miami.

147. Hawa is not planning to become an actor, nor is Teresa or Kathleen, since they both have lunch with the acting student (1, 2). Ming must be the student planning to become an actor. Since Hawa and Ming sat for paintings by the art student (1), then either Kathleen or Teresa is the artist. However, since Hawa has never seen Teresa, then Teresa must not be the artist; Kathleen is. Neither Ming nor Kathleen can be the singer, since they both saw the singer perform, so Hawa must be the singer. This leaves Teresa as the dancer.

Summary: Kathleen—artist; Hawa—singer; Ming—actor; Teresa—dancer

148. Jerry is either Jess's sibling or Kit's brother-in-law (2). Based on statement 2, Jerry cannot be the same gender as Jess's sibling. Thus, Jerry must be Kit's brother-in-law. It follows that Jerry is a man, Jess is likely his spouse, and Kit is Jess's sibling. Jess and Kit are sisters (2).

Summary: Jerry (male) is married to Jess (female). Jess and Kit are sisters; Jerry is Kit's brother-in-law.

149. Dan is older than Dominica but younger than Danil. Danil is younger than Dennis, making Dennis the oldest.

Summary: Dennis, Danil, Dan, Dominica

150. Clifford is not the navigator's name (1, 4). Passenger Leon doesn't live nearest the navigator (2, 5). Since neither passenger Clifford nor passenger Leon lives nearest the navigator, and since the navigator lives halfway between Boston and Los Angeles (6), and since passenger Clifford lives in Boston, passenger Leon must live in Los Angeles. This makes Leon the navigator (1). Testa

is not the copilot, since she played with him in racquetball (3), and Testa is not the navigator, so Testa is the pilot. Clifford is thus the copilot.
Summary: Testa is the pilot; Clifford is the copilot; Leon is the navigator.

151. (This solution involves algebraic equations and the related transposition of terms.) Let L = amount Luis picked, E = amount Ellie picked, T = amount Tran picked, and S = amount Selina picked. Use the following inequalities: (1) E > L + T *or* E > L and E > T (2) L + E = T + S *or* L = T + S − E (3) L + S > E + T. Substituting (2) into (3) gives S > E. Using this last inequality, we get: S > E > L > T (since L + E = T + S, and if S > E, then L > T).
Summary: In order of the amount of berries each person picked, from the highest to the lowest, the names are Selina, Ellie, Luis, and Tran.

152. The waiter can't be guilty, since all of Ms. Berg's statements would be true. Ms. Hernandez is not guilty, since Ms. Berg's second and third statements would be false. Ms. Mason is not guilty, since either she or Ms. Hernandez would have two false statements. Ms. Berg is the guilty person.

153. Keisha and Drew are dancing, but Keisha is not Drew's date (Jamal is dancing with her) (5, 4). Therefore, neither Keisha, Becky, nor Shira (none of whom are dancing with Jamal) can be Drew's date. This makes Lydia Drew's date. Since Jamal is dancing with Lydia, and statement 1 says that Lydia is dancing with Becky's date, Becky must have come to the prom with Jamal. Since Charlie is dancing with Jamal's date (Becky), and Becky is dancing with Shira's date (3), then Charlie and Shira came to the prom together. This leaves LeBron and Keisha as the final pair.
Summary: Drew went with Lydia; Charlie went with Shira; Jamal went with Becky; LeBron went with Keisha.

154. A simple chart works well here to help students keep track of the data:

	Artistic	Runner	Languages	Scientist
Allie	✔	✔	✗	✗
Grace	✗	✔	✗	✔
Elena	✔	✗	✔	✗
Page	✗	✗	✔	✔

When as many boxes as possible have been filled in according to statements 1–5, students can fill in the rest by recalling that only *two* students will have each of the characteristics listed in the chart.
Summary: Allie—artistic and a runner; Grace—a runner and a scientist; Elena—artistic and good at languages; Page—good at languages and a scientist

155. There are three true statements only if Misha took the candy bar. Then the statements of Octavius, Jack, and Alex are true, while the statements of Misha and Dan are false.

156. Again, students may find that a chart can help them organize their data for this puzzle. Mr. Chinn is the author (5), Mr. Gates is the gardener (1, 2), and Mr. Reyes is the musician (1, 2). Mr. Chinn is not the bookkeeper (4) and not the firefighter (3), so he must be the cab driver. Mr. Reyes is not the firefighter (6), so he must be the bookkeeper. Mr. Gates is therefore the firefighter.
Summary: Mr. Chinn—author and cab driver; Mr. Gates—gardener and firefighter; Mr. Reyes—musician and bookkeeper

157. The Dodge didn't finish fourth, because that would have forced the Toyota and the Honda to finish first and second (2, 4), contradicting statement 1. The Dodge didn't finish second, because that would have forced the Toyota and Honda to fill, between them, the fourth and fifth place—which, since the Volvo didn't finish third (3), would contradict statement 1. Therefore, the Dodge finished third (5); it follows that neither the Honda nor the Toyota finished second or fourth (2, 4). Since the Honda didn't finish first (1), it finished fifth; hence, the Toyota finished

first, and the Volvo finished fourth (1). The Ford finished second.

Summary: First—Toyota; second—Ford; third—Dodge; fourth—Volvo; fifth—Honda

158. Since the manager is married and has a grandson (5), the manager cannot be Mr. Brown, Mr. Campbell, Ms. Britos, or Ms. Womack. Mr. DaSilva is the manager's neighbor (4). Therefore, the manager can only be Ms. Liu. Of the two remaining women, one must be the bagger, who is female (3), but it clearly is not Ms. Britos. Thus, the bagger is Ms. Womack. Ms. Britos, the remaining unassigned female worker, cannot be the cashier or assistant manager, since both jobs are held by men (2, 5), nor can she be the bookkeeper, who has a son-in-law (2). Therefore, Ms. Britos is the clerk. Mr. DaSilva must be the bookkeeper, since the bookkeeper has a son-in-law, and Mr. Campbell and Mr. Brown are too young (1, 2). Since the cashier is a son-in-law, and therefore is married, it cannot be Mr. Brown; the cashier is thus Mr. Campbell. This leaves the only remaining unassigned male, Mr. Brown, as the assistant manager.

Summary: Ms. Liu—manager; Ms. Womack—bagger; Ms. Britos—clerk; Mr. DaSilva—bookkeeper; Mr. Campbell—cashier; Mr. Brown—assistant manager

159. Jesse must be the painter (3). He is not the writer (2), the cook (6), the musician (5), or the gardener (5), so he must be the hairstylist; Jesse is the painter and the hairstylist. Dan must be either the musician or the gardener (5), but he can't be the gardener (1), so he must be the musician. Dan is also not the cook (4), so he must be the writer; Dan is the musician and the writer. By elimination of the other occupations, Azad is the cook and the gardener.

Summary: Jesse—painter and hairstylist; Dan—musician and writer; Azad—cook and gardener

160. Carmen's last name is not Doyle (2), nor is Joe's (3), or Gustav's (3); Mary's last name is therefore Doyle. Carmen's last name is not Fong (5), not Sanchez (3), and not Doyle (Mary's name), so it is

Perry. Since Joe's last name is not Sanchez (6), it is Fong; Gustav's last name is Sanchez. Gustav must be the naval enlistee (1). Carmen is not the certified public accountant (2), not the teacher (4), and not naval trainee (Gustav); Carmen is thus the lawyer. Joe is not planning to become a teacher (6), so he must be planning to become a certified public accountant, and Mary is planning to become a teacher.

Summary: Carmen Perry—lawyer; Joe Fong—certified public accountant; Mary Doyle—teacher; Gustav Sanchez—naval trainee

161. Since the heights of young Lin, young Fox, the flute player, and the saxophone player (1, 2, 3, 4) are not equal to the height of the clarinet player, then the height of young Ortiz is equal to that of the clarinet player (5). Young Ortiz has exactly twice as many records as the clarinet player, so she can't be the daughter of the saxophone player, who has an odd number of records (7), and she isn't the daughter of the flute player (6), so she must be the daughter of the clarinet player. Thus,

Ms. Ortiz is the clarinet player.

162. Emilio's sibling is the guilty party (5), so Emilio is innocent, as is Tessa (Emilio's wife). Tucker cannot be Emilio's sibling, because he has met Emilio's mother only once (4), so Tucker is innocent. Although Mandy had been in the hospital before the accident (2), she is not in the hospital any longer; she therefore caused the accident, and she is Emilio's sister.

Since the hostess, Tessa, was asked to give some information about the guilty person (8), she must be alive. Since Mandy caused the accident, Mandy is not the victim. This leaves either Emilio or Tucker as the victim. Since Tucker has had his leg in a cast for over a year (3), and Mandy has known Tessa for only six days (7), Tucker and Mandy are the people with whom Tessa does not customarily play tennis (1). Therefore, one of them must have eaten with Emilio on the previous night (6). Mandy, however, caused the accident, so it is not she. Tucker must have eaten with

Emilio, so Tucker is the victim.
Summary: Mandy accidentally killed Tucker.

163. The head linesman is not Enzo or Juan (4, 5) and not Roy (1, 6); it is Jack. Roy is not the head linesman (Jack), nor is he the umpire (7, 9), so he is the referee (3, 8). The field judge is either Enzo or Roy (1, 2), but since Roy is the referee, Enzo is the field judge. This leaves Juan as the umpire.
Summary: Enzo—field judge; Juan—umpire; Jack—head linesman; Roy—referee

164. The dentist's daughter is not Denise or Maria (3), so it is Saira. Dr. Alvarez is not the physician (2), and Dr. Kahn is not the physician (1), so Dr. Reed is the physician. Maria is not the physician's (Dr. Reed's) daughter or Dr. Alvarez's daughter (2), so she must be Dr. Kahn's daughter. Denise (by elimination) is the professor's daughter. Since Maria is not Dr. Alvarez's daughter and not the physician's (Dr . Reed's) daughter (Denise)(2), Dr. Alvarez's daughter must be Saira. Dr. Alvarez is thus the dentist; Dr. Kahn is the educator.
Summary: Dr. Alvarez—dentist, daughter Saira; Dr. Kahn—professor, daughter Maria; Dr. Reed—physician, daughter Denise

165. Colin does not live in California (1) and not in Georgia (3), so he must live in Rhode Island; he cannot drive a Camry (1), and he cannot drive the RAV4 (2), so he must drive the GMC Suburban. Gabe doesn't live in Georgia (1) and can't live in Rhode Island, because that is where Colin lives, so he must live in California; he doesn't drive the GMC Suburban (1) and he doesn't drive the Camry (2), so he must drive the RAV4. By elimination, Rueben is from Georgia and drives the Camry.
Summary: Colin—Rhode Island, GMC Suburban; Gabe—California, RAV4; Rueben—Georgia, Camry

166. Brian is obviously a boy's name, and since the student whose surname is Jankowitz is male (4), Brian's surname must be Jankowitz. Emily's surname is not Cox (1) and not Jankowitz (Brian), so it is Wong; Marisa's surname is therefore Cox. The girl whose surname is Wong (Emily) is not

doing the Internet research (2), so Marisa is the girl doing the Internet research; since Brian is not doing the interviews (3), he must be doing the editing and writing, and Emily is doing the interviews.
Summary: Brian Jankowitz—editing and writing; Emily Wong—interviews; Marisa Cox—Internet research

167. The freshman boy is David (2). The student whose surname is Chinn is in a class above Tanya and in a class below Mary Lou (3), so since David is a freshman, Tanya must be a sophomore, student Chinn must be a junior, and Mary Lou must be a senior. Student Chinn, who must be male (3), is Nando. The student whose surname is Hayes is a senior (4), so Hayes must be Mary Lou's surname. Since the student whose surname is Kyros is a girl (1), then this must be Tanya's surname. David's surname (by elimination) is Freitas.
Summary: Nando Chinn—junior; David Freitas—freshman; Mary Lou Hayes—senior; Tanya Kyros—sophomore

168. The Bishops' daughter is Greta, and their speedboat is *Molly* (4). The Laytons' daughter is Julia, and their speedboat is the *Monica* (2, 5). Monica's family is not the Parks (3) or the LaCasses (2, 3), so the Zilkhas are Monica's family and their speedboat is the *Anisa* (6). The Parks' daughter is Anisa (3, 6), and their speedboat is the *Greta*. By elimination, the LaCasses' speedboat is the *Julia*, and their daughter is Molly.
Summary: The Bishops own *Molly*, and their daughter is Greta; the LaCasses own *Julia*, and their daughter is Molly; the Zilkhas own *Anisa*, and their daughter is Monica; the Laytons own *Monica*, and their daughter is Julia; the Parks own *Greta*, and their daughter is Anisa.

169. The student from Wisconsin must be Kate (7). Ahmed is not from Michigan (5), not from Kentucky (3), and not from Wisconsin (Kate), so he is from Ohio. David is from Michigan (5), so Rosa (by elimination) is from Kentucky. Student Peterson is not from Ohio (1, 4), nor is student Gomez (2), nor is student Evans (4);

student Rashid is therefore from Ohio, and this is Ahmed. Student Evans is not Kate (4), not Rosa (6), and not Ahmed (Rashid), so it must be David. Kate's surname is not Peterson (1, 4), so it must be Gomez; Rosa's surname is therefore Peterson.

Summary: Ahmed Rashid—Ohio; David Evans—Michigan; Kate Gomez—Wisconsin; Rosa Peterson—Kentucky

170. (*Note:* The solutions provided here are not necessarily the only correct solutions.) The chairperson is not Ali, Becca, Dan, Felipe, Gabe, or Imani, since Becca, Gabe, Hamdi, and Imani would be telling the truth. The chairperson is not Charlie, since Becca, Charlie, Dan, and Felipe would be telling the truth. The chairperson is not Emma, since Ali, Emma, Gabe, and Hamdi would be telling the truth. This leaves Hamdi. Indeed, he is the chairperson, and only Becca, Dan, and Gabe are telling the truth.

171. Since Janet arrives home with her mother, then Janet's mother gets home ten minutes before her usual time, thereby spending ten minutes less time driving. Thus, her mother must spend five minutes less time going to the station and five minutes less time returning home. Since her mother meets Janet five minutes from the station (and five minutes ahead of the usual time), Janet must have walked for twenty-five minutes.

172. Neither Sophie nor Karim plays first (3, 7) and Josh does not play first (7), so Beth must play first. Sophie does not play second (7), and Josh does not play second (7), so Karim plays second. Sophie plays third (7), and Josh plays fourth.

The student whose number is 3 is not Beth (6), since Beth plays first. It is also not Josh (4), so it is either Karim or Sophie. However, according to statement 6, the person with the number 3 plays before Josh (number 6). Therefore, Sophie must be number 3. That makes Karim number 11 and Beth number 16 (by elimination). Karim does not have fifteen houses (5), and Sophie does not have fifteen houses (2). Thus, Beth has fifteen houses.

Summary: Beth plays first and is number 16; Karim plays second and is number 11; Sophie plays third and is number 3; Josh plays fourth and is number 6.

173 . Since the young women changed the first letters of their last names when they married (3), the newlywed Ms. Painter must originally have been either Ms. Glazier or Ms. Locksmith. However, since Mr. Locksmith Sr. is not a locksmith (no father has a trade suggested by his name), she must have been Ms. Glazier, and Mr. Locksmith Sr. must be a glazier by trade.

Mr. Painter Sr. cannot be a painter, and he is not a plumber (1), so he must be a glazier or a locksmith. However, the newlywed Ms. Painter was formerly Ms. Glazier, so Mr. Painter Sr. must be a locksmith. Since Mr. Plumber Sr. cannot be a plumber, and is not a glazier (Mr. Locksmith) or a locksmith (Mr. Painter), he must be a painter. Mr. Glazier Sr. is therefore a plumber.

Mr. Painter Jr. is not a painter, not a locksmith (his father's trade), and not a glazier (his wife's birth name), so he is a plumber. Mr. Locksmith Jr. is not a locksmith, not a glazier (his father's trade), and not a plumber (Mr. Painter Jr.), so he is a painter. Similarly, Mr. Glazier Jr. is a locksmith, and Mr. Plumber Jr. is a glazier.

Ms. Locksmith does not marry young Mr. Locksmith (3), not young Mr. Painter (Ms. Glazier's husband), nor young Mr. Glazier (since her father is a glazier), so she must be young Mr. Plumber's wife. Similarly, Ms. Painter is young Mr. Glazier's wife, and Ms. Plumber is young Mr. Locksmith's wife.

Summary: Mr. Glazier, Sr.—plumber, son's trade is locksmith, son's wife is Ms. Painter; Mr. Locksmith Sr.—glazier, son's trade is painter, son's wife is Ms. Plumber; Mr. Painter Sr.—locksmith, son's trade is plumber, son's wife is Ms. Glazier; Mr. Plumber Sr.—painter, son's trade is glazier, son's wife is Ms. Locksmith

174. If one student has all of the answers wrong, then six of the remaining answers by the other three students must be correct. Since no answers by the

students to a specific question are the same three times, then the correct answers must appear twice for two of the answers (to provide the six correct answers). Only when Charles's answers are considered all wrong does this situation exist.

It follows that the correct answer to question number 1 is *France*, and the correct answer to question number 3 is *Germany* (since these answers appear twice in the responses of the other three students). Since the correct answer to question number 2 can't be *Italy* (because Charles's answer is *Italy*) and it is not *France* (since *France* is the correct answer to question number 1), it must be *England*. This leaves *Italy* for the correct answer to question number 4. **Summary:** The answers are *France*, *England*, *Germany*, and *Italy*, respectively.

175. Let *a*, *b*, and *c* represent the names provided in the statements. The statements can now be expressed as follows:

Names	City of Residence	City Where Teacher Teaches
Oakland	?	Piedmont
a	Alameda	Oakland
b	Piedmont	a
Berkeley	?	b
c	?	?

Since a name can appear in any line across or down only once, then *a* = Hayward, *b* = Alameda, and *c* = Piedmont. Thus, the teacher named Piedmont must teach in Berkeley.

176. Ms. Day is not a resident of Evansville (2), nor is Mr. Traverse (2), nor is Mr. Evans (initial *E*), nor is Ms. Pitt (1); Mr. Louis must therefore live in Evansville. Ms. Pitt lives in Traverse City (1). Mr. Evans doesn't live in Louisville (3), or Pittsburg (3), or Evansville (Mr. Louis), or Traverse City (Ms. Pitt); he therefore lives in Dayton.

Mr. Evans is not a lawyer (3), nor is Ms. Pitt (1), or Mr. Louis (initial *L*), or Mr. Traverse (2); Ms. Day is therefore the lawyer. Since Ms. Day is the lawyer, she cannot live in Louisville, and she doesn't live in Dayton (letter *D*), or Evansville (2), or Traverse City (Ms. Pitt); she therefore lives in Pittsburg, and Mr. Traverse (by elimination) lives in Louisville.

Since Ms. Pitt lives in Traverse City (1), she is not the teacher (initial of city), and she is not the plumber (letter *P*), or the electrician (1), or the lawyer (Ms. Day); she must be the doctor. Mr. Louis lives in Evansville, so he is not the electrician, nor is Mr. Evans (letter *E*), nor is Ms. Day (the lawyer), or Ms. Pitt (the doctor); thus Mr. Traverse is the electrician. Since the teacher doesn't live in Dayton (4), he must live in Evansville; this is Mr. Louis. The plumber lives in Dayton; this is Mr. Evans.
Summary: Ms. Day—lawyer, Pittsburg; Mr. Evans—plumber, Dayton; Mr. Louis—teacher, Evansville; Ms. Pitt—doctor, Traverse City; Mr. Traverse—electrician, Louisville

177. Teacher Antonio is not student Antonio's teacher; teacher Bell is not student Bell's teacher; and teacher Chatterjee is not student Chatterjee's teacher (1). Teacher Bell is not student Chatterjee's teacher (3), so teacher Antonio must be student Chatterjee's teacher. Teacher Chatterjee is therefore student Bell's teacher, and teacher Bell is student Antonio's teacher.

Student Chatterjee does not go to English class (3), so his teacher (teacher Antonio) does not teach English. Student Antonio's teacher does not teach English (6); thus, the English teacher is teacher Chatterjee. Student Antonio's teacher (teacher Bell) does not teach history (6), so teacher Antonio teaches history and teacher Bell teaches math. Thus, student Antonio goes to math (his teacher is the math teacher), student Bell goes to English (his teacher is the English teacher), and student Chatterjee goes to history.

Daily Warm-Ups: Logic

The senior is student Chatterjee, the history student (2); the math student (student Antonio) is not the sophomore (4), so Antonio must be the junior, and student Bell is the sophomore. **Summary:** Student Antonio—math, junior; student Bell—English, sophomore; student Chatterjee—history, senior. Ms. Antonio is the history teacher; Mr. Bell is the math teacher; Ms. Chatterjee is the English teacher.

178. Earl's team defeated Kennedy by four points (3) and did not play Washington (1), so his team is either Lincoln or Jefferson. Jermaine's team was in the finals, but lost (2). Since Earl's team won its first game, his team must have played in the finals against Jermaine's team and won in overtime by one point. Since Rob's team lost to the undefeated team (5), his team must be Kennedy (3). The red team lost to Lincoln in the semifinals (6) by one point (7), so Lincoln must be the other team in the finals. Lincoln's captain must be Jermaine, and the team jerseys are orange (7).

Earl's team did not play Washington (1), so Washington must be the red team that played Lincoln (6); its team captain, by elimination, would be Enrique. Also by elimination, Earl's team would be Jefferson. Since Jermaine did not see his cousin play, his cousin must have been the captain of Kennedy, which has green jerseys (4). By elimination, the color of Jefferson's jerseys is blue. **Summary:** Jefferson—captain is Earl, blue jerseys, won in semifinals over Kennedy by four points, won in overtime final over Lincoln by one point; Kennedy—captain is Rob, green jerseys, lost in semifinals to Jefferson by one point; Lincoln—Jermaine is captain, orange jerseys, won in semifinals over Washington by one point, lost in overtime final to Jefferson by one point; Washington—Enrique is captain, red jerseys, lost in semifinals to Lincoln by one point.

179. Jamal should be able to assure himself a winning combination if he takes one chip from the middle pile on the first turn.

180. To win consistently, plan to arrive at the number 89 as the last number before you write 100. To assure being able to write 89, you must watch for the opportunity to provide a total of 23, 34, 45, 56, 67, or 78, then add numbers such that the sum of your opponent's entry and your entry is 11.

Turn downtime into learning time!

Other books in the

Daily *Warm-Ups* series:

- Algebra
- Algebra II
- Analogies
- Biology
- Character Education
- Chemistry
- Commonly Confused Words
- Critical Thinking
- Earth Science
- Geography
- Geometry
- Journal Writing
- Math Word Problems
- Mythology
- Physics
- Poetry
- Pre-Algebra
- Prefixes, Suffixes, & Roots
- Shakespeare
- Spelling & Grammar
- Test-Prep Words
- U.S. History
- Vocabulary
- World Cultures
- World History
- World Religions
- Writing